CW00419141

Giacomo Leopardi
1798–1837

Giacomo Leopardi

Dialogue Between Fashion and Death

TRANSLATED BY GIOVANNI CECCHETTI

PENGUIN BOOKS — GREAT IDEAS

PENGUIN BOOKS

Published by the Penguin Group
Penguin Books Ltd, 80 Strand, London WC2R ORL, England
Penguin Group (USA) Inc., 375 Hudson Street, New York, New York 10014, USA
Penguin Group (Canada), 90 Eglinton Avenue East, Suite 700, Toronto, Ontario,
Canada M4P 2Y3 (a division of Pearson Penguin Canada Inc.)
Penguin Ireland, 25 St Stephen's Green, Dublin 2, Ireland (a division of Penguin Books Ltd)
Penguin Group (Australia), 250 Camberwell Road, Camberwell, Victoria 3124, Australia
(a division of Pearson Australia Group Pty Ltd)
Penguin Books India Pvt Ltd, 11 Community Centre, Panchsheel Park,
New Delhi – 110 017, India
Penguin Group (NZ), 67 Apollo Drive, Rosedale, North Shore 0632, New Zealand
(a division of Pearson New Zealand Ltd)
Penguin Books (South Africa) (Pty) Ltd, 24 Sturdee Avenue, Rosebank, Johannesburg 2196,
South Africa

Penguin Books Ltd, Registered Offices: 80 Strand, London WC2R ORL, England

www.penguin.com

First published as *Operette Morali / Essays and Dialogues*
by the University of California Press, 1982
Published in Penguin Books 2010

1

Copyright © The Regents of the University of California, 1982

This selection published by arrangement with the University of California Press, 2010
All rights reserved

Set in 11/13 pt Dante MT Std
Typeset by TexTech International
Printed in England by Clays Ltd, St Ives plc

ISBN: 978-0-141-19255-0

www.greenpenguin.co.uk

Contents

Dialogue
Between Hercules and Atlas

HERCULES. Father Atlas, Jove sends me and wants me to
bring you his greetings, and in case you are tired of
that burden, he wants me to take it on my shoulders
for a few hours, as I did I don't remember how many
centuries ago, so that you can catch your breath and
rest a little.

ATLAS. I thank you, my little Hercules; I also feel much
obliged to His Majesty Jove. But the world has become
so light that this cloak I wear to protect myself from
the snow is much heavier. And if it weren't that Jove
forces me to stand still here, balancing this little ball
on my back, I'd put it under my arm or in my pocket,
or I'd let it dangle from a hair of my beard, and then
I'd go about my business.

HERCULES. How has it gotten so light? I can see that it
has changed shape and that it has become like a bread
roll, and it's no longer round as it was when I studied
cosmography for that enormous voyage with the
Argonauts, but still, I don't understand why it should
weigh less than it used to.

ATLAS. I don't know the reason either. But you can verify
its lightness yourself if you take it in your hand for a
moment and feel its weight.

HERCULES. By Hercules, if I hadn't felt it myself, I could
never have believed it. But what kind of novelty is this

that I discover? The last time I carried it, it throbbed strongly on my back, like the heart of an animal, and it made a continuous buzzing roar that sounded like a hornet's nest. But now, it ticks like a watch with a broken spring; and it doesn't make the slightest buzz of any kind.

ATLAS. I can't explain this either except that a long time ago the world stopped giving signs of any motion and noise; and, personally, I had a very strong suspicion that it was dead, and from day to day I expected to be infected with its stench. So I was trying to figure out how and where I could bury it and the kind of inscription I should put over its grave. But when I saw that it didn't rot, I concluded that from the animal that it was at first it had turned into a plant, like Daphne and many others, and that this was the reason it didn't stir or breathe. And even now I am afraid that it will soon put down roots and plant them into my shoulders.

HERCULES. I rather believe that it is asleep and that this sleep is of the same kind as that of Epimenides, which lasted more than half a century; or that of Hermotimus, whose soul, they say, used to leave his body whenever it wanted to and remain absent for many years, happily wandering about various countries and then coming back – until his friends, to put an end to such pranks, burned the body. And so when the spirit returned to get back into its home, it found it destroyed, and if it wanted a lodging, it had either to rent another one or to go to an inn. But to make sure that the world will not sleep forever and that some friend or benefactor won't set it on fire, thinking that it is dead, I say that we should try to wake it up.

ATLAS. Good. But how?

HERCULES. I'd let it have a good whack of my club; but I am afraid I'd thoroughly flatten it into a pancake; or perhaps I'd crack it like an egg since its shell feels so light that it must have become quite thin. And I'm not so sure that men, who used to fight lions with their bare hands, and now fight fleas, wouldn't all faint away from the blow. The best thing is for me to get rid of my club and for you to take off your cloak and then for us to play ball with this tiny globe. I'm sorry I haven't brought the gauntlets or rackets Mercury and I use when we play in Jove's house or his back yard, but our fists should be enough.

ATLAS. Good idea! And what if your father, seeing us play, feels like joining us in the game and throws one of his fireballs and makes us tumble – who knows where – just like Phaethon into the Po?

HERCULES. True, if, like Phaethon, I were a poet's son and not his and if I weren't such that – while poets peopled the cities by the sounds of their lyres – I could unpeople heaven and earth by the sound of my club. And with a kick I would send his fireball flying all the way to the last ceiling of the Empyrean. But you can be sure that even if I got it into my head to unnail five or six stars for a game of cobnuts or to do target shooting with a comet and use it as a sling by holding it by the tail or even to use the sun itself in discus throwing, my father would pretend not to see. Then, in this game our intention is to do good to the world, and it

3

is not like that of Phaethon, who wanted to show off his agility to the hours, who held his stepping block when he climbed into the cart and who also wanted to gain the reputation of being a good charioteer with Andromeda and Callisto and with the other fair constellations, to whom, as we are told, he flung in passing bouquets of rays and candied little balls of light. In fact, he wanted to make a show of himself before the gods during their promenade that day, which, as you know, was a holiday. So don't worry about my father's being angry; in any case, I promise that I will pay you the damages. Now let's get going. Take off your cloak and throw the ball.

ATLAS. Like it or not, I'd better do as you say; you're strong and armed, and I'm old and without weapons. At least be careful not to let it fall so that it doesn't get any more bumps and doesn't get bruised or cracked, as when Sicily broke off from Italy and Africa from Spain; or a splinter may tear off – like a province or a kingdom – and there may be a war as a result.

HERCULES. Don't worry.

ATLAS. Your turn to serve. Don't you see that it's limping because it's out of shape?

HERCULES. Come on. Hit it harder; your serves don't reach me.

ATLAS. It's not the hitting; the wind comes from the southwest, as is usual here, and the ball is carried by the wind – it's so light.

HERCULES. It's the same old story; always chasing after the wind.

ATLAS. Actually, it wouldn't be a bad idea to inflate it, for

4

it doesn't bounce off the fist any more than a melon does.

HERCULES. This is a new flaw, for in ancient times it bounced and jumped like a mountain goat.

ATLAS. Run! Quick! Quick! I say. Don't let it fall; damn the moment you came here!

HERCULES. You served it to me so badly and so low that I couldn't have caught it even if I'd broken my neck running. Oh, poor thing, how are you? Did you hurt yourself? I can't hear anyone breathing; I can't see a soul stirring; they're all still asleep.

ATLAS. Let me have it, by all the horns of the Styx, so that I may settle it again on my shoulders. And you pick up your club, and go back to heaven as fast as you can, and apologize for me to Jove for this accident, which was all your fault.

HERCULES. I'll do so. For many centuries a certain poet by the name of Horace has been a guest in my father's house, where he was admitted as court poet upon the recommendation of Augustus, who had been deified by Jove out of consideration for the power of the Romans. This poet keeps singing certain songs of his; in one of them he says that a just man remains unmoved even if the world falls. I must think that now all men are just, for the world has fallen and no one has moved.

ATLAS. Who ever doubted the justice of men? But stop wasting time; run and hurry to clear me with your father; for I am afraid that at any moment a thunderbolt will turn me from Atlas into Etna.

Dialogue
Between Fashion and Death

FASHION. Madam Death, Madam Death.

DEATH. Wait for your time, and I'll come without your calling me.

FASHION. Madam Death.

DEATH. Go to hell. I'll come when you don't want me.

FASHION. As if I weren't immortal.

DEATH. Immortal?

'More than a thousand years have passed' since the time of the immortals.

FASHION. Oh, our Madam spews Petrarch too, just like a sixteenth- or nineteenth-century Italian poet.

DEATH. I love Petrarch's poetry because there I find my Triumph and because it mentions me almost everywhere. But now get out of my way.

FASHION. Come, in the name of your love for the seven deadly sins, stop a moment and look at me.

DEATH. I'm looking.

FASHION. Don't you recognize me?

DEATH. You should know that I don't see very well and that I can't wear glasses because the English don't make any that fit me, and even if they did, I wouldn't know how to keep them on.

FASHION. I'm Fashion, your sister.

DEATH. My sister?

FASHION. Yes. Don't you remember that we are both Caducity's daughters?

DEATH. What can I remember, I who am memory's greatest enemy?

FASHION. But I remember well; and I know that you and I together keep undoing and changing things down here on earth although you go about it one way and I another.

DEATH. If you are not talking to yourself or to someone who is inside your throat, raise your voice and chisel your words better; if you keep mumbling between your teeth with that spider-web voice of yours, I'll never hear you, for if you don't know it already, my hearing is no better than my eyesight.

FASHION. Even if it isn't good manners – and in France people don't speak in order to be heard – and since we are sisters and don't have to stand on ceremony, I'll speak as you want. I'm saying that it is our nature and our custom to keep renovating the world. But right from the start you threw yourself on people and on blood, whereas I'm generally satisfied with beards, hair, clothes, furnishings, buildings, and the like. It is quite true, however, that I haven't refrained – nor am I refraining now – from playing many games comparable with yours, such as, for instance, piercing ears, lips, or noses with holes and causing them to be torn by the trinkets I hang in those holes; charring the flesh of men with red-hot brands, as I make them do for beauty's sake; misshaping the heads of babies with bandages and other trappings, making it a custom for all the men of a country to have their heads in the same shape, as I have done in America and in Asia; crippling people with tight shoes; cutting off their breath and making their eyes pop out because of their tight corsets; and a hundred other such things. As a matter of fact and generally speaking, I persuade and force all genteel men to endure daily a thousand hardships and a thousand discomforts and often pain and torment and I even get some of them to die gloriously for love of me. I won't tell you about the headaches, the colds, the inflamations of all kinds, the quotidian, tertian, or quartan fevers that men catch to obey me, agreeing to shiver in the cold or to stifle in the heat according to my wishes, by protecting their shoulders with wool and their chests with cloth, and by doing everything my way, no matter how much it hurts them.

DEATH. Then I believe that indeed you are my sister and, if you want me to, I'll hold it more certain than death itself – without your having to prove it with a parish birth certificate. But if I keep this still, I'll faint. So, if you feel like running next to me, be sure you don't croak, for I go fast; and as we run, you can tell me about your business. Or else, in view of our family ties, I promise you that upon my death I'll leave you everything I have, and you can stay where you are with my best wishes.

FASHION. If we were to run the Palio together, I don't know which one of us would win the race, for whereas you can run, I can go faster than a gallop; and whereas you faint by standing still in one place, I waste away. So let's start running again, and, as you say, as we run, we'll talk about our affairs.

DEATH. Let's get on with it. And since you were born from my mother's womb, it would be good if you would help me in some way with my chores.

FASHION. I have done that in the past more often than you think. First of all, though I continuously cancel and distort all the other customs, I've never in any place allowed the practice of dying to stop; and because of this, you can see it going on everywhere from the very beginning of the world until today.

DEATH. Some miracle – that you didn't do what you couldn't.

FASHION. What do you mean I couldn't? Obviously you don't seem to know the power of fashion.

DEATH. All right, all right! We'll have plenty of time to talk about that when the custom of not dying has come. But for the moment I would like you, as a good sister, to help me obtain the opposite goal more easily and more speedily than I have done so far.

FASHION. I have already told you about some of my doings that are of great assistance to you. But they are trifles in comparison with what I am going to tell you now. A little at a time, but mostly during these past years, to help you out, I have caused the neglect and the elimination of the exertion and those exercises which favor physical well-being, and I have introduced innumerable others that weaken the body in a thousand ways and shorten life and have caused them to be valued highly. In addition to this, I have put in the world such orders and such customs that life itself, both of the body and of the soul, is more dead than alive, so much so that this century can truly be called the century of death. And while in ancient times you had no other property except ditches and caves – where you sowed bones and dust in the darkness, which are seeds that bear no fruit – now you have land in the sun; and the people who move and walk about with their own feet are, so to speak, entirely yours even without harvesting them – as a matter of fact from the very moment they are born. Furthermore, if in the past you were generally hated and reviled, nowadays, because of my doings, things have come to such a point that whoever has any intelligence values and praises you, preferring you to life, and loves you so much as to call you constantly and to look to you as their greatest hope. Finally, I saw many boasting that they would become immortal, that is to say, they would not die completely because a good part of them would not fall into your hands. Although I knew that this was nonsense and that if those or any other people lived in the memory of mankind, their life would become a joke and they wouldn't enjoy their fame any more than they would suffer from the humidity of their tombs – in any case, seeing that this business of immortality stung you, because it seemed to injure your honor and your reputation – I have done away with this custom of seeking immortality and also of bestowing it on anyone who might deserve it. So now if someone dies, you can rest assured that there isn't a particle of him that isn't dead, and he'd better go right underground in his entirety, just like a fish who's swallowed up head and bones in a mouthful. These things are neither few nor slight, and I have done them for your sake – as I wanted to advance your domain on earth, as has happened. For this purpose I am ready to do the same, and more, each day; and for this reason I looked for you. And I think it desirable that from now on we should always stay together, for in this manner we'll be able to talk things over and reach the best decisions, as well as carry them out.

DEATH. You are quite right. Let's do as you say.

Dialogue Between
the Earth and the Moon

EARTH. My dear Moon, I know that you can speak and answer questions because you are a person, as I have often heard from the poets. Also, our children say that you, in fact, have a mouth, nose, and eyes, just like their own, and this they can see with their very eyes, which, at their age, must naturally be extremely sharp. As for me, I have no doubt that you know that I am no less a person, so much so that when I was younger, I had many children, so you will not be surprised if you hear me speak. Well then, my sweet Moon, although I have been your neighbor for so many more centuries than I can remember, I never said a word to you until now, for I was so busy with my chores that I did not have any time left for a chat. But now my affairs are of very little consequence; as a matter of fact, I can state that they take care of themselves. I don't know what to do, and I'm bored to death. So I plan to talk to you often in the future and to take an interest in your affairs – if I don't trouble you too much.

MOON. Don't worry about that. I wish Fortune would give me as little trouble as I am certain you will give me. If you feel like talking to me, talk as much as you want, for although I am a friend of silence, as I think you know, I shall listen to you and shall be happy to answer your questions if that can be of help to you.

EARTH. Do you hear this delightful music, which the heavenly bodies make with their movements?

MOON. To tell you the truth, I don't hear anything.

EARTH. I don't hear anything either, except the roar of the wind rushing from my poles to the equator and from the equator to my poles – and it doesn't seem anything like music. Yet Pythagoras says that the celestial spheres make a certain music, so sweet that it is indeed wondrous and that you yourself have a part in it, for you are the eighth string of this universal lyre, which I don't hear because I am deafened by that very music.

MOON. Then I must surely be deafened too, for, as I said, I don't hear it; and I didn't know I was a string.

EARTH. Then let's change the subject. Tell me, are you really inhabited, as so many philosophers, ancient and modern, from Orpheus to De La Lande, state and swear? Though, like a big snail, I try to stretch these horns of mine, which men call mountains and peaks and with whose tips I keep staring at you, I have never been able to discover a single inhabitant on you – and yet I hear that one David Fabricius, whose eyesight was keener than that of Linceus himself, once discovered a number of them as they were hanging their laundry in the sun.

MOON. As to your horns, I don't know anything. The fact is that I'm inhabited.

EARTH. What color are those men of yours?

MOON. What men?

EARTH. Those who inhabit you. Didn't you say you are inhabited?

MOON. Yes. And so?

EARTH. And so, your inhabitants cannot all be animals.

MOON. Neither animals nor men, though I don't know what kind of creatures they are – either of them. As a matter of fact, I haven't been able to understand an iota of what you have been saying about men, as I think you call them.

EARTH. But what kind of people are yours?

MOON. Very many and different kinds; you don't know them just as I don't know yours.

EARTH. That is very strange to me, so much so that if I hadn't heard it from you yourself, I could not believe it for anything in the world. Have you ever been conquered by any of your inhabitants?

MOON. Not that I know of. And how? And why?

EARTH. Through ambition, through greed for other people's possessions, by means of politics, by force of arms.

MOON. I do not know what you mean by arms, ambition, politics; in short, I don't know what you are talking about.

EARTH. But if you don't know about arms, you certainly know about war, for not long ago, one of our scientists with the help of a telescope – which is an instrument made to see very far – discovered a great fortress up there with regular and straight bastions, which is a sign that your people are at least acquainted with sieges and mural combats.

MOON. Excuse me, Madame Earth, if I answer you a little more freely than becomes one of your subjects or servants, as I am. But really, you strike me as rather vain if you think that all things in every part of the world are like your own; as if Nature were only intent on reproducing you in everything she did. I say that I am inhabited, and from this you conclude that my inhabitants must be men. I inform you that they are not; and although you accept the fact that they are different creatures, you assume that they have the same qualities and live under the same conditions as your people; and you bring up the telescope of some scientist or other. But if this telescope doesn't see more clearly in other cases than in this one, I must believe that its eyesight is as good as your children's, who discover in me eyes, mouth, nose – which I don't know anything about.

EARTH. Then it isn't true that in your provinces there are broad-paved roads and that you are cultivated – as can be clearly seen from the German regions with a telescope.

MOON. If I am cultivated, I don't know anything about it. And as to my roads, I do not see them.

EARTH. My dear Moon, you must know that I am somewhat dense and slow, and no wonder men fool me so easily. But I can tell you that even if your own people have never tried to conquer you, nonetheless, you weren't always free from danger; for at various times many people down here got it into their heads to conquer you themselves, and for that purpose they made plans and preparations. But even though they climbed to the highest points and raised themselves on their tiptoes and stretched out their arms, they could not reach you. Moreover, I have seen for many years men minutely scrutinize every part of you, drawing maps of your regions, and measuring the height of your mountains, which we even know by name. I thought I should tell you these things out of my affection and consideration for you so that you'd be prepared for any emergency. Now, let me ask you a couple of questions. How annoyed are you by the dogs barking at you? What do you think of those who point you out in wells? Are you male or female? In ancient times people were not quite sure. Is it true that the Arcadians came into the world before you? That your women – or whatever I should call them – are oviparous, and that one of their eggs fell down here some time ago? And that you are pierced in the middle like rosary beads, as a modern scientist believes? That you are made of green cheese, as the English say? That one day, or perhaps one night, Mohammed cut you in half, just like a watermelon, and that a large chunk of your body slipped into his sleeve? How happy are you to sit on the tops of minarets? How do you feel about the feast of Bairam?

MOON. Go right ahead. When you go on like this, I don't need to answer you and break my usual silence. If you like to spend your time with such nonsense and cannot find anything else to talk about, instead of turning to me who cannot understand you, you'd do better to get men to build you another planet, made and inhabited the way you like, to whirl around you. You can't talk of anything else but men, dogs, and other such things, about which I know no more than about that gigantic sun, around which they say our own sun revolves.

EARTH. Truly, as I talk to you, the more I resolve to avoid speaking about my own things, the less I succeed. But from now on, I'll try to be more careful. Tell me, are you the one who enjoys making the water of my seas rise and then enjoys letting it fall?

MOON. Maybe. But supposing I do to you this or anything else, I don't notice it at all, as in the same way you probably don't notice your influence up here, which must be much greater than mine on you, as you are greater in size and strength.

EARTH. Actually, the only thing I know about the influence I have on you is that every once in a while I take away the light of the sun from you, and I take away your own light from myself. I also know that during your nights I shine very brightly on you, as I myself can see at times. But I was forgetting something that is more important than anything else. I would like to know if really, as Ariosto writes, everything that man loses – such as youth, beauty, health, the labors and the expenses invested in learning and in gaining fame, in bringing up children according to the norms of good behavior, in founding or promoting useful institutions – everything goes and collects up there so that all human things can be found in you, except folly, which never leaves mankind. If this is true, I suppose you must be so full that you have no room to spare, especially if we consider that in recent times men have lost a great many things (such as patriotism, virtue, magnanimity, integrity), not only in part and not only a few of them, as happened in the past, but all together and completely. And certainly, if those things are not up there, I don't know in what other place they could be found. Therefore, I would like to make a pact with you. You'll start returning all these things to me now, and then you'll keep doing so as the opportunity arises. After all, I think that you yourself would be glad to be rid of them, especially common sense, which, as I understand, takes a tremendous amount of space. I would see to it that every year men would pay you a substantial sum of money.

MOON. And there you speak of men again. Although, as you state, folly does not leave your regions, you seek men's wits while you try to take my own away from me. I don't know where they are, if they are disappearing or if they remain in any part of the world; all I know is that they cannot be found here, just as one cannot find any of the other things you have been asking about.

EARTH. At least you can tell me if up there people are acquainted with vice, crime, calamity, pain, old age, in short, evils. Do you understand these words?

MOON. Oh yes. I surely understand them. And not only the words but the things they mean; I know them perfectly well, for I am filled with them – rather than with the other things you mentioned.

EARTH. What are more prevalent among your people, virtues or vices?

MOON. Vices, by far.

EARTH. What is more abundant, good or evil?

MOON. Evil, without comparison.

EARTH. And, in general, your inhabitants are happy or unhappy?

MOON. So unhappy that I wouldn't change places with the most fortunate of them.

EARTH. It's the same here. So much so that it is a great surprise how similar you are to me in this, whereas you are so different in everything else.

MOON. I am also similar to you in form, and in movement, and in receiving light from the sun, and this is no less surprising than the rest because evil is something common to all the planets of the universe or at least of this solar system – just as much as roundness and the other conditions I have mentioned. If you could raise your voice so high that it could be heard by Uranus or Saturn, or by any other planet of our world, and if you could ask them whether unhappiness exists on them and whether good or evil prevails among them, each would answer in the same way I have. I say this because I have already asked Venus and Mercury about the same things, for now and then I find myself closer to them than you. I have also asked some of the comets that have passed by me. All have answered in the same way as I have. And I believe that the sun himself, and every star, would give the same answer.

EARTH. In spite of all this, I am still hopeful, especially nowadays, when men are promising me great future happiness.

MOON. Hope as much as you like; I assure you that you can hope forever.

EARTH. Do you know what's going on? These men and these animals are beginning to stir and make noise. On the side from which I'm talking to you, it is night, as you can see, or rather, as you can't see; and so they were all asleep, and at the commotion that we are making while we talk, they are waking up with great fear.

MOON. But up here, as you can see, it is daytime.

EARTH. I don't want to frighten my people or to shatter their sleep, which is the greatest blessing they have. So we'll talk again some other time. Goodbye, then; and good day.

MOON. Goodbye; and good night.

The Wager of Prometheus

In the year eight hundred thirty-three thousand two hundred and seventy-five of the reign of Jove, the College of the Muses ordered that certain posters be printed and affixed in the public places of the city and suburbs of Hypernephelus, by which all the gods, great and small, as well as the other inhabitants of the city, who recently or in former times might have made some valuable discovery, were invited to present it, either in person or in the form of a model or a description, to the judges appointed by said College. At the same time, regretting that because of their well-known poverty they could not be as generous as they would have liked, they promised, as a prize to the competitor whose invention would be judged the most beautiful and the most useful, a laurel crown with the privilege of wearing it day and night, in public and in private, within and without the city, along with the right to be painted, sculpted, engraved, molded, that is, represented in any manner and material, with such a laurel crown on the head.

Many of the gods competed for this prize, just as a pastime, something no less necessary to the inhabitants of Hypernephelus than to those of other cities – not that they had any desire for that crown, which was not worth a cotton nightcap; and as for glory, if men themselves, now that they have become philosophers, despise it, we can imagine in what kind of esteem it is held by the gods, who are so much wiser than men (as a matter of fact, according to Pythagoras and Plato, they are the only ones to be really wise). Therefore – and it was a unique example, until then unheard of for similar cases of awards offered to the most deserving – this prize was adjudged without the intrusion of solicitations or favors, of secret promises or intrigues. Three competitors won: Bacchus for the discovery of wine; Minerva for the discovery of oil, which is so necessary to the gods for daily anointing after their baths; and Vulcan for having invented an economical copper pot, by which any food can be cooked quickly and with little fire. So the prize had to be divided into three parts, with the result that each one got a small laurel branch; and all three of them refused it, either in part or in whole. Vulcan declared that as most of his time was spent working and sweating before the fire of his forge, that thing on his forehead would be a great nuisance – not to mention that it would expose him to the danger of being burned or scorched if a spark should by chance fall upon those dry leaves and set them on fire. Minerva said that since she had to hold on her head a helmet large enough to cover at once the armies of a hundred cities, as Homer writes, it was not advisable for her to increase that weight in any way. Bacchus said that he didn't want to change his hat and his crown of vine leaves for a laurel crown, although he would happily accept it if he were allowed to use it as a sign in front of his tavern. But the Muses refused to grant it to him for this purpose so that it remained in their treasury.

The other competitors did not envy the three deities

who had won and had rejected the prize, nor did they complain about the judges or blame their decision, except one, Prometheus, who had entered the competition by sending in the clay model which he had used in forming the first men, adding to it a description of the qualities and functions of the human race, which he had invented. No little astonishment was caused by Prometheus's dissatisfaction in this matter, which all the others, winners and losers alike, had taken as no more than a game. But as the reason for such dissatisfaction was investigated, it was learned that he strongly desired not the honor itself but the privilege he would have enjoyed had he been the winner. Some think that he wanted to avail himself of the laurel to protect his head against the storms, as we are told of Tiberius, who, whenever he heard thunder, put on his crown, for he believed that laurel was not susceptible to lightning. But in the city of Hypernephelus there is neither thunder nor lightning. Others, more plausibly, state that Prometheus, who was getting on in years, was beginning to lose his hair – a misfortune which he, like many others, did not like at all – and since he had not read Synesius's work in praise of baldness or, as is more likely, since he had not been convinced by it, he wanted to conceal the bareness of his head under the diadem, just as Julius Caesar did.

But to go back to our story. One day, as he was talking to Momus, Prometheus bitterly complained that wine, oil, and pots had been given preference over the human race, which he pronounced the best work the immortals had brought to the world. And since he thought that Momus was not convinced, for he advanced all kinds of arguments to the contrary, Prometheus suggested that both of them fly down to earth together and in each of its five parts stop at random in the first place they discovered to be inhabited by men; but first they made this mutual wager – with Prometheus betting that in all of the five places, or in the majority of them, they would find positive proof that man is the most perfect creature in the universe. This was acceptable to Momus, and having agreed on the amount of the wager, they immediately began their descent toward the earth. They first directed themselves to the New World, for owing to its very name and owing to the fact that no one of the immortals had ever been there, it especially excited their curiosity. They made their first stop in the northern area of the country of Popaián, not far from the river Cauca, in a place where there appeared many signs of human habitation – traces of cultivation in the countryside, numerous trails, although often interrupted and mostly obstructed, trees felled and stretched out on the ground, and particularly what looked like graves, with some human bones here and there. But for all that, the two celestial creatures could neither hear a man's voice nor see a live man's shadow no matter how much they sharpened their ears or their eyes. They went on, partly walking, partly flying, for many miles, passing over mountains and rivers, and everywhere they found the same signs and the same solitude. 'How is it these places are so deserted,' said Momus to Prometheus, 'when they clearly show that they were inhabited?' Prometheus mentioned tidal waves, earthquakes, hurricanes, heavy rains, which he knew to be common in tropical regions; and, indeed, at that very time they heard in all the nearby forests rain constantly falling from the tree branches as they were shaken by the wind. But Momus could not possibly understand how that area could be subject to tidal waves – the sea being so far away that it could nowhere be seen; and he could understand still less how it had happened that earthquakes, hurricanes, and heavy rains had destroyed all the men of that country while they had spared jaguars, monkeys, foxes, anteaters, eagles, parrots, and a hundred other kinds of animals of the earth and of the air, which were visible in the area. Finally, as they descended into an immense valley, they discovered, as it were, a small heap of houses, or rather of wooden huts, covered with palm leaves – each one surrounded by a wooden fence. In front of one of them there were many people, some standing, some sitting around an earthen pot suspended over a large fire. The two celestial beings, having taken human form, approached the group. Prometheus courteously greeted everybody and then turned to the one who appeared to be the chief and asked him what they were doing.

SAVAGE. We're eating, as you can see.
PROMETHEUS. Do you have something good to eat?
SAVAGE. Only this meat.
PROMETHEUS. Is it meat from a domestic or from a wild animal?
SAVAGE. Domestic; as a matter of fact, from my own son.
PROMETHEUS. Did you have a steer for a son, like Pasiphae?

SAVAGE. Not a steer but a man, such as all other people have.

PROMETHEUS. Do you really mean it? Do you eat your own flesh?

SAVAGE. Not my own but certainly his, for it was only for this purpose that I brought him into the world, and I cared for him and nurtured him.

PROMETHEUS. Just for the purpose of eating him?

SAVAGE. What's so strange? And his mother too! Since she is not likely to bear any more children, I'm planning to eat her soon.

MOMUS. Just as you eat the hen after having eaten the eggs.

SAVAGE. And so the other women I have . . . as they become useless for childbearing . . . I'll eat them too. And these slaves you see here . . . do you think I'd keep them alive if every once in a while I didn't get some of their children to eat? But as they get old, I'll eat them too, one at a time – if I live long enough.

PROMETHEUS. Tell me, those slaves – do they belong to your own people or to another?

SAVAGE. To another.

PROMETHEUS. To one very far from here?

SAVAGE. Very far, so much so that between their houses and ours there was a little stream.

Then he pointed at a low hill and added: 'There, that's where they used to live, but our people destroyed them.' At this point Prometheus noticed that many of the savages were ogling him with the kind of loving look that a cat gives a mouse. Thus, so as not to be eaten by his own creatures, he quickly took off in flight; and so did Momus with him. Both of them were so scared that as they departed, they contaminated the barbarians' food with the same kind of dirt that the Harpies out of envy showered on the tables of the Trojans. But the savages, more hungry and less squeamish than Aeneas's companions, continued their meal.

Prometheus, quite disappointed with the New World, immediately directed his course toward the oldest world, that is to say, toward Asia; and having covered in not much more than an instant the distance between the new and the ancient Indies, both of them made their descent near Agra, in a field overflowing with a vast multitude of people gathered on the edge of a trench crammed with wood – on whose brim you could see on one side some men with lighted torches, ready to set the wood afire, and on the other, on a platform, a young woman wearing extremely sumptuous clothes and all kinds of barbaric ornaments, who was dancing and shouting and showing signs of the most extravagant joyfulness. As he saw this, Prometheus imagined a new Lucretia or a new Virginia, or an emulator of Erechtheus's daughters, of Iphigenia, of Codrus, of Menecius, of Curtius, and of Decius, who, following the command of some oracle, would voluntarily offer herself up in sacrifice for her country. When he later learned that the woman was sacrificing herself because of her husband's death, he thought that she, not unlike Alcestis, wanted to buy back her husband's life at the price of her own. But having further ascertained that she was preparing herself to be burned alive only because this was the custom among the widows of her group, that she had always hated her husband, that she was drunk, and that the dead man, rather than coming back to life, was to be burned in that very same fire, Prometheus immediately turned his back on that spectacle and headed for Europe. On the way, he held this conversation with his companion.

MOMUS. Would you ever have thought, when with enormous risk you stole fire from heaven to give it to men, that some of them would use it to cook one another in pots and some others to burn themselves voluntarily to death?

PROMETHEUS. Certainly not. But don't forget, dear Momus, that those we have seen so far are barbarians and that the nature of men should not be judged from barbarians but from civilized people toward whom we are now traveling. I'm firmly convinced that among them we'll see and hear things that not only will seem worthy of praise but will also fill you with astonishment.

MOMUS. If men are the most perfect species in the universe, I don't see why they need to be civilized in order not to burn themselves to death or not to eat their own children. The other animals are all barbarians, and yet they don't deliberately burn themselves, except the phoenix, who has never been seen by anyone; those who eat any of their own kind are extremely rare, and still rarer are those who feed on their own offspring – and then only because of some strange accident and not because they've brought them into the world for this purpose. Note also that of the five parts of the world, only one, by far the smallest and not even all of it, plus some minimal areas of another part, are endowed with that civilization that you acclaim. And I don't think that you yourself will maintain that this civilization is so complete that nowadays the men of Paris or of Philadelphia have reached all the perfection of which their species is capable. Now, how long did those people have to work and suffer to reach a state of civilization which is not yet perfect? as many years as those that can be counted from the origin of man to our day. And almost all the inventions that were either most necessary or most conducive to the attainment of a civilized state have had their origins not in design but in chance so that human civilization is more the work of accident than of natural development; and where those accidents have not occurred, the people are still barbarians, although they are just as old as the civilized ones. Therefore, I conclude, if barbarians show themselves in many ways inferior to any other animal; if civilization, which is the opposite of barbarism, is even today the prerogative of a small part of the human race; and if, additionally, this small part has been able to reach the present civilized condition only after innumerable centuries, and mostly by accident rather than by any other cause; and finally, if this condition is far from being perfect – I wonder if you would consider that your judgment of the human race might be more correct if you shortened it in this manner, that is to say, by stating that the human race is indeed supreme among all the others, as you think, but supreme in imperfection rather than in perfection – although men, in speaking and in judging, continually mistake one for the other, for they draw their conclusions from premises which they have themselves devised and which they hold to be tangible truths. It is certain that the other species of creatures have been totally perfect from the very beginning, each according to its own nature. And even if it weren't clear that a savage, considered in relation to the other animals, is the worst of all, I fail to understand why being extremely imperfect in one's own nature, as man appears to be, should be valued as a greater condition of perfection than that of all other creatures. We should add that human civilization, which is so difficult to attain, and perhaps impossible to bring to completion, is not so stable that it cannot disintegrate, as has, in fact, happened many times and among various people who had acquired a good measure of it. In short, I am of the opinion that if your brother Epimetheus had brought before the judges the model he must have used when he formed the first donkey or the first frog, he would have perhaps won the prize you couldn't get. However, I'll be happy to concede that man is a most perfect creature if you decide to say that his perfection is like the one Plotinus attributed to the world, which, said Plotinus, is excellent and perfect in absolute; but to be perfect, the world must contain, among other things, all possible evils as well; for, in fact, we can find in it as much evil as it can possibly hold. And in this sense, I would probably also concede to Leibniz that the present world is the best of all possible worlds.

There is no doubt that Prometheus had a ready answer – clear, precise, and logical – to all these arguments; but it is equally certain that he did not produce it; for at that very moment they found themselves over the city of London. They descended and saw a great multitude of people gathering by the door of a private house. They joined the crowd and entered the house; there they found a man lying on his back in a bed with a pistol in his hand; he was dead, a wound in his chest; and next to him lay two small children, also dead. Several members of the house staff were also in the room, as well as some magistrates, who were questioning them, while a clerk wrote down their answers.

PROMETHEUS. Who are these wretched people?

A SERVANT. My master and his children.

PROMETHEUS. Who killed them?

SERVANT. My master, all three of them.

PROMETHEUS. You mean to say, his children and himself?

SERVANT. Yes!

PROMETHEUS. Incredible! Something really terrible must have happened to him.

SERVANT. Not to my knowledge.

PROMETHEUS. But perhaps he was poor, despised by everyone, disappointed in love, or in disfavor with the Court.

SERVANT. On the contrary! He was very rich, and I think everyone held him in high esteem; to love he was indifferent, and he was very much in favor with the Court.

PROMETHEUS. Then, how did he get so desperate?

SERVANT. Because of the tedium of life, as he has declared in writing.

PROMETHEUS. And these magistrates – what are they doing?

SERVANT. They are inquiring whether my master had lost his mind or not; for if he hadn't, his property goes to the Crown; and indeed there is no way to avoid that.

PROMETHEUS. But tell me, had he no friend or relative to whom he could entrust these small children instead of killing them?

SERVANT. Yes, he did, and, among others, one to whom he was especially close and to whom he has entrusted his dog.

Momus was about to congratulate Prometheus on the good effects of civilization and on the happiness which it seemed to bring to men's lives; he also wanted to remind him that no other animal, except man, kills himself voluntarily or takes the lives of his own children out of sheer desperation. But Prometheus was ahead of him and, without caring about seeing the two remaining parts of the world, paid him the wager.

Dialogue Between
Nature and an Icelander

An Icelander, who had traveled most of the world and had visited many different countries, was once wandering in the interior of Africa when he crossed the equator into a region never before explored by man. There he met with an adventure similar to the one encountered by Vasco da Gama, when he doubled the Cape of Good Hope and the Cape itself, which stands guard over the Austral seas, came toward him in the form of a giant to dissuade him from entering those uncharted waters. The Icelander saw an enormous bust far away in the distance. At first he imagined it to be made of stone, like those colossal figures he had seen on Easter Island many years before. But as he drew nearer, he discovered that it was the huge body of a woman, seated on the ground, her bust erect and her back and her elbow resting against a mountain. And she was not a statue, but alive – her face at once beautiful and awesome, her eyes and her hair raven black. She looked at him fixedly for some time, without speaking. Finally she said:

NATURE. Who are you? What are you looking for in these regions, where so far your species has been unknown?

ICELANDER. I'm a poor Icelander and am fleeing Nature. I have fled her nearly all my life in a hundred areas of the earth, and now I'm fleeing her in this area.

NATURE. So flees the squirrel from the rattlesnake until he finally falls into its jaws. I am she from whom you're fleeing.

ICELANDER. Nature?

NATURE. No one else.

ICELANDER. I regret it to the depths of my soul, for I firmly believe that no greater misfortune could happen to me.

NATURE. You should have known that I would be found especially around these parts, where, as you know, my power is more evident than elsewhere. But what prompted you to run away from me?

ICELANDER. Let me tell you that since my early youth and after a little experience, I became aware and convinced of the vanity of life and of the stupidity of men, who fight one another continually for pleasures that don't please and for goods that don't help; they endure and inflict on one another innumerable worries and innumerable troubles, which actually harass and injure; and thus the more they seek happiness, the farther away they get from it. As a result of these perceptions, I abandoned all other desires and resolved to lead an obscure and quiet life, without bothering anyone, without trying to advance myself in any way, without competing with anyone for any good in the world. And without hoping for any kind of pleasure – which is something that's denied our species – I did not set for myself any other goal than to stay away from suffering. With this I don't mean to say that I intended to abstain from work and physical labor, for, as you well know, there is a difference between labor and discomfort and between a quiet and an idle life. As soon as I began to carry out this resolution, I learned by experience how vain it is to think that if you live among men and you don't hurt anyone, you may also avoid being hurt by others; and that if you spontaneously withdraw and are satisifed with the minimum, you may be allowed a little place somewhere, and this minimum may not be taken away from you. But I easily freed myself from the hostility of men by removing myself from their society and by retiring into solitude – which in my native island can be accomplished without difficulty. After doing this and living almost without any trace of pleasure, I still could not exist without suffering because the intense cold of the long winters and the extreme heat of the summers, which are typical of that region, tormented me continually; and the fire, next to which I was forced to spend much of my time, dried up my flesh and tortured my eyes with smoke so that neither inside my house nor in the open air could I save myself from perpetual discomfort. Nor could I lead that quiet life to which I especially turned all my aspirations, for the frightening storms on land and sea, the rumblings and the threats of Mount Hekla, the fear of fires, which are extremely frequent in wooden houses such as ours, never ceased to disturb me. In a constantly uniform life, divested of all desires and hopes and of almost all worry but that of being in peace and quiet, such discomforts as these assume no little weight and are far more serious than they usually appear to be when most of the mind is occupied by thoughts of social

35

and civil life and by the adversities produced by men. Thus, when I found that the more I withdrew and almost contracted myself, as it were, within myself so as not to disturb or harm anything in the world, the less could I avoid being troubled and tormented by other things, I began to change regions and climates to see if there was any part of the earth where, offending no one, I might escape being offended and where, not enjoying pleasure, I might escape suffering. I was further moved to this resolution by the thought that perhaps you had destined the human race to only one climate of the earth (as you had done with each of the other species of animals and plants) and to certain specific areas outside of which men could neither prosper nor live without difficulty and misery; so that if they should scoff at and exceed the limits that your laws had prescribed for human dwellings, such difficulty and misery were to be blamed on them, and not on you. I have searched almost the entire world and have explored almost every country, always keeping my resolution of causing other creatures the least possible trouble and of seeking only a quiet life. But I was burned by heat in the tropics, stiffened by cold near the poles, afflicted by the instability of the weather in the temperate zones, plagued everywhere by the convulsions of the elements. I have seen many places where not a day passes without a storm, which is like saying that every day you attack and give deliberate battle to those inhabitants who have never done you any harm. In other regions the usual serenity of the sky is balanced by the frequency of earthquakes, by

the multitude and the fury of volcanoes, by the sub-
terranean boiling and rumbling of the entire country.
Winds and furious tornadoes prevail in the regions
and the seasons that are free from the other furies of
the weather. There were times when I felt the roof
cave in over my head because of the great weight of
the snow; other times, because of the torrential rain,
the earth itself cracked and gave away under my feet.
At times I had to flee as fast as I could from rivers that
pursued me as if I had done them some wrong. Many
wild beasts I had never provoked with the slightest
offense tried to devour me; many snakes tried to poi-
son me; in various places flying insects almost consumed me to the bone. I won't speak of the infinite
number of daily dangers, which are always threaten-
ing man, so much so that an ancient philosopher could
not find any cure for fear other than the fact that everything is to be feared. Nor was I spared by illnesses
although I was, and still am, not only temperate but
self-denying in the pleasures of the flesh. I greatly
marvel when I consider that you have instilled in us
such a strong and insatiable craving for pleasure that
without this pleasure and deprived of what it naturally
desires, our life is most imperfect; and yet you have
ordered that the indulgence in this pleasure shall be,
of all things human, the most harmful to the strength
and the health of the body, the most calamitous to
everyone, and the most contrary to the duration of
life itself. Nevertheless, although I have almost always
and completely abstained from all pleasures, I could
not avoid suffering many and diverse illnesses, some

of which brought me to the brink of death; others threatened me with the loss of a limb or with perpetually leading a more miserable life than in the past; and all of them oppressed my body and mind for days and months with a thousand privations and a thousand sufferings. Although in times of illness each of us experiences new and unfamiliar pains and greater unhappiness than normal (as if human life were not sufficiently miserable as it is), you certainly have not compensated man for this by giving him periods of exuberant and unusually good health, which could bring him some extraordinary pleasure both in quality and in quantity. In countries that are generally covered with snow, I was nearly blinded, as regularly happens to the people of Lapland. The sun and the air, which are vital and necessary to our life and therefore, inescapable, continuously abuse us – the air with its humidity, its rigor, and its other whims, the sun with its heat and with light itself, so much so that man can never be exposed to either one of them without some degree of discomfort or harm. Indeed, I can't remember spending one single day of my life without suffering, whereas I cannot even count those days that I have passed without the shadow of a pleasure. I realize that suffering is as much our inevitable fate as is lack of pleasure and that it is as impossible to lead a quiet life of any kind as it is to lead a restless one without misery; thus, I am bound to conclude that you are a manifest enemy of men, and of the other animals, and of all your own creatures. Now you ensnare us, now you threaten us, now you attack us, now you sting us, now

you strike us, now you rend us, and always you offend
or persecute us. Either by habit or by rule, you are the
slaughterer of your own family and of your own children and, as it were, of your own flesh and blood.
Therefore, I have no more hope. I have understood
that men finally stop persecuting those who flee or
hide from them with the firm resolution of fleeing
and hiding, but you never stop harrowing us until you
finally crush us. And I am already close to the bitter
and gloomy time of old age, a true and manifest evil,
in fact an accumulation of the most oppressive evils
and miseries, an evil which is not accidental but destined by your laws to all kinds of living creatures,
foreknown by each of us from childhood, and continuously apparent in us from our twenty-fifth birthday
on, with a sad and unfortunate process of unmerited
decay. So that one-third of man's life is assigned to
growth, only a few instants to maturity and perfection, and the rest to decline, with all the resulting discomforts.

NATURE. Did you think by any chance that the world was
made for you alone? Now let me tell you that in my
works, laws, and operations, except for very few of
them, my purpose was not, and is not, the happiness
or unhappiness of men. When I harm you in any way
and with whatever means, I don't notice it, except very
rarely; just as I ordinarily don't know whether I please
or help you; nor have I done those things, nor do I do
those actions, as you believe, to please or to help you.
Finally, even if I happened to wipe out your entire species, I wouldn't notice it.

ICELANDER. Let us suppose that someone of his own initiative invited me and strongly urged me to visit his villa, that to please him I accepted, and that once there, I was to be lodged in a dilapidated and ruined cell, humid, fetid, and exposed to the wind and the rain, where I was in constant danger of being crushed. And that not only did he not take the trouble to entertain me with some recreation or provide me with some comfort, but he barely furnished me with enough to keep alive, and he also let me be reviled, scorned, threatened, and beaten by his children and by the rest of his family. And if I complained to him of such treatment, he answered: 'Do you think that I built this villa for you or that I keep these children and these servants of mine just to assist you? I have many things to think about other than entertaining you and spending money for your support.' To this I would reply: 'See, my friend, as you did not build this villa for me, so it was your privilege not to invite me here. But since you asked me of your own initiative to come and stay here, don't you think you should arrange it so that, as far as possible on your part, I should be able to live here without suffering and without danger?' This is what I am saying now. I know very well that you did not create the world for the service of men; I could more easily believe that you created it for the express purpose of torturing them. Now I ask you, did I ever beg you to put me in this universe? Did I intrude into it violently and against your will? Indeed, you yourself have placed me here with your own hands and of your own will and without my knowledge and in such a way that I could neither resist nor oppose it. Then is it not your duty, if not to keep me happy and satisfied in this kingdom of yours, at least to see to it that I am not tormented and tortured and that living in it is not harmful to me? And what I am saying about myself, I am also saying about the entire human race, about the other animals, and about all living creatures.

NATURE. Evidently, you have not considered that in this universe life is a perpetual cycle of production and destruction – both functions being so closely bound together that one is continuously working toward the other, thus bringing about the conservation of the world, which, if either one of them were to cease, would likewise dissolve. Therefore, were anything free from suffering, it would be harmful to the world.

ICELANDER. That is just what all philosophers say. But since what is destroyed suffers and what destroys does not experience pleasure and is itself soon also destroyed, tell me what no philosopher can: who finds any pleasure or who finds any advantage in this most miserable life of the universe, which is preserved by means of the suffering and the death of the very things that compose it?

We are told that while they were engaged in these and similar discussions, there happened to appear two lions who were so worn out and starved that they barely had enough strength to eat up the Icelander, which they did and thus managed to get enough nourishment to survive for the rest of that day. But there are some who deny this story and maintain that while the Icelander was speaking, an extremely fierce wind arose, threw him down to the ground, and raised over him a majestic mausoleum of sand, under which, perfectly desiccated and turned into a beautiful mummy, he was later discovered by some travelers and placed in the museum of a European city.

Dialogue
Between Frederick Ruysch and His Mummies

Chorus of Mummies
in Frederick Ruysch's Study

Alone in the world, eternal, toward whom does move
Every created thing,
In you, Death, finds rest
Our naked nature;
Not joyous, but secure
From ancient suffering. Profound
Night in our confused mind
Obscures our grave thought;
Towards hope, desire, the shriveled spirit
Feels its strength wane;
Thus from affliction and from fear is freed
And the empty slow years
Unbored whiles away.
We lived; and as the confused memory
Of a frightening ghost
And of a sweating dream
Wanders in the souls of infants,
So in us remembrance lingers
Of our lives: but far from fear
Is our remembering. What were we?

What was the bitter point called life?
Stupendous mystery is today
Life to our minds, and such
As to the minds of the living
Unknown death appears. As when living
From death it fled, now flees
From vital flame
Our naked nature
Not joyous but secure;
For to be happy
Is denied to mortals and denied the dead by Fate.

RUYSCH. (*Outside his study, looking through the chinks of the door*) What's going on? Who taught music to these dead? They sing like roosters in the middle of the night. I'm in a cold sweat and am almost more dead than they are. I didn't expect them to come back to life simply because I preserved them from decomposition. Well, for all my philosophy I'm shaking from head to foot. Damn that devil who made me bring these people into my house. I don't know what to do. If I keep them locked up here, they might break the door down, or they might get out through the keyhole and come and get me in my bed. To call for help because I'm afraid of dead people doesn't look good. All right, a little courage, and let me try to scare them instead.

(*Entering*) Eh, children, what kind of game is this? Don't you remember that you are dead? What's this racket you are making? Have you gotten cocky because of the Czar's visit, and do you think you're no longer subject to the same laws as in the past? I suppose you meant all this in jest, and no more. If you've come back to life, I congratulate you; but I'm not rich enough to support the living the same way I support the dead; therefore, you'll have to go. If what they say about vampires is true, and you are vampires, you'll have to look for some other blood to drink; for I'm not going to let you suck mine, no matter how generous I've been with the artificial blood I've put into your veins. In short, if you want to keep quiet and silent, as you have so far, we'll remain on good terms, and in my house you won't go without anything you need; otherwise, I'm going to get the door bar and kill you all.

MUMMY. Don't be upset; I promise you that we'll all stay as dead as before, without your having to kill us.

RUYSCH. Then what's this idea of singing?

MUMMY. A short time ago, at exactly midnight, for the first time that great mathematical year has ended of which the ancients write so much; and this is also the first time the dead speak. And not only us but in every cemetery, in every tomb, down at the bottom of the sea, under snow or sand, in the open air, or in whatever place they are, at midnight, all the dead sang, like ourselves, that little song you heard.

RUYSCH. And how long will they go on singing or talking?

MUMMY. As for singing, they have already finished. For talking, they'll be allowed a quarter of an hour. Then they'll return to silence until that same year is again completed.

RUYSCH. If that's true, I don't think you'll break my sleep again. Talk together freely. I'll stand aside and gladly listen to you out of curiosity without disturbing you.

MUMMY. We can only talk by answering some living person. After the song is finished, those who don't have to answer the living remain quiet.

RUYSCH. I'm really sorry, for I think it would be great fun to hear what you'd say among yourselves if you could talk together.

MUMMY. Even if we could, you wouldn't hear anything; for we wouldn't have anything to say to one another.

RUYSCH. I can think of a thousand questions to put to you. But since time is short and leaves no choice, let me know in brief what kind of sensations of body and mind you experienced at the point of death.

MUMMY. I didn't notice the actual point of death.

THE OTHER MUMMIES. We didn't either.

RUYSCH. How come you didn't notice it?

MUMMY. Just as you never notice the moment you begin to sleep, no matter how much attention you pay.

RUYSCH. But to fall asleep is natural.

MUMMY. And don't you think that dying is natural? Show me a man, or an animal, or a plant that doesn't die.

RUYSCH. I'm no longer surprised that you go on singing and talking if you didn't notice when you died.

> Unwitting of the blow, he went ahead,
> Combatting still, and yet already dead,

writes an Italian poet. I thought that on this question of death, those like you would know something more than the living. But going back to our subject, at the point of death didn't you feel any pain?

MUMMY. What kind of pain can it be if one who feels it doesn't notice it?

RUYSCH. At any rate, all are convinced that the sensation of death is extremely painful.

MUMMY. As if death were a sensation and not the opposite.

RUYSCH. Yet in regard to the nature of the soul, both those who incline to the opinion of the Epicureans and those who hold the common belief, all, or most of them, agree with what I am saying, that is, in believing that death is by its very nature and beyond all comparison an extremely acute pain.

MUMMY. Well, just ask both of them on our behalf: if man has no power to notice the point when his vital operations, to a greater or lesser extent, remain only interrupted by sleep, lethargy, syncope, or by whatever cause, how will he notice the point when those same operations cease altogether, and not for a short space of time but forever? And moreover, how can it be that a living sensation exists in death? As a matter of fact, how can it be that death itself is by its very nature a living sensation? When the power of feeling is not only weak and scanty but reduced to such a minimum that it fails and is abolished, do you think that a person is capable of a strong sensation? In fact, do you believe this very extinction of the power of feeling to be in itself a very great sensation? You can observe that as death approaches, even those who die of acute and painful diseases sooner or later, before they expire, become calm and rest so that we can perceive how, being reduced to a small quantity, their life is no longer sufficient for pain, and as a result pain ceases sooner than life itself. This you may tell on our behalf to whoever thinks he'll die of pain at the point of death.

RUYSCH. Those reasons might be enough for the Epicureans. But not for those who judge otherwise of the substance of the soul, as I have done in the past and will do much more in the future, having heard the dead speak and sing. For believing that death consists in a separation of the soul from the body, they will not understand how these two things, conjoined and, as it were, conglutinated together in such a way that they both form only one person, can be separated without very great violence and unspeakable suffering.

MUMMY. Tell me, is the spirit by any chance attached to the body by some nerve or by some muscle or membrane, which must necessarily be torn when the spirit goes? Or is it by any chance part of the body, from which it must be violently snatched or severed? Don't you see that the soul leaves the body only because it is not allowed to remain and has no place there any longer and not because of any force that tears it and uproots it? Tell me also, when the soul enters the body, does it by any chance feel stuck and vigorously fastened or, as you say, conglutinated to it? Why then, when it leaves that body should the soul feel itself being detached or, in other words, experience a most violent sensation? Rest assured that the entry and the exit of the soul are equally quiet, easy, and soft.

RUYSCH. Then what's death if it's not pain?

MUMMY. Pleasure rather than anything else. You should know that dying, like falling asleep, does not take place in an instant but by degrees. True, these degrees are more or less and greater or smaller according to the variety of the causes and to the kinds of death. In the last moment death brings neither pain nor pleasure, no more than does sleep. In the preceding moments it cannot produce pain because pain is something alive, and, at that time, that is, after the beginning of death, man's senses are moribund, which is like saying weakened in the extreme. It may well be a cause of pleasure, for pleasure is not always something alive; in fact, most human pleasures consist in some sort of languor, so that man's senses are capable of pleasure even when they are near extinction since very often languor itself is pleasure, especially when it frees you from suffering; for, as you well know, the cessation of any pain or discomfort is in itself pleasure. So, the languor of death ought to be the more welcome as it frees man from greater suffering. Personally, although in the hour of death I didn't pay much attention to what I was feeling because the doctors had ordered me not to tire my brain, I nevertheless remember that the sensation I experienced was not much unlike the pleasure produced in men by the languor they feel while they are falling asleep.

THE OTHER MUMMIES. We also seem to remember that.

RUYSCH. Be it as you say, although all those with whom I have had the chance of discussing this matter had an altogether different opinion; but then, so far as I can remember, they didn't bring up their own personal experience. Now tell me, at the time of death, while you felt that pleasure, did you think you were dying and that that pleasure was a courtesy of death, or did you imagine something else?

MUMMY. So long as I wasn't dead, I never thought I wouldn't escape that danger; and at least up to the last moment that I had the power to think, I kept hoping that I would still have an hour or two of life, as I think happens to many when they die.

THE OTHER MUMMIES. The same thing happened to us.

RUYSCH. Indeed, Cicero says that no one is so decrepit that he doesn't expect to live at least another year. But how did you notice at last that the spirit had left the body? Tell me, how did you know that you were dead? They don't answer. Children, don't you hear me? The quarter of an hour must be over. Let me feel their pulse. They're dead again all right; there is no danger of their scaring me another time. So let's go back to bed.

Dialogue
Between Christopher Columbus
and Pedro Gutierrez

COLUMBUS. A beautiful night, my friend.

GUTIERREZ. Beautiful indeed; but I think it would be more beautiful seen from land.

COLUMBUS. Good. So you're tired of sailing too.

GUTIERREZ. Not just of sailing; but this sailing is turning out to go on much longer than I thought, and it's beginning to get to me. Even so, you shouldn't think that I'm complaining about you, as the others do. Rather, you can be sure that whatever you may decide in regard to this voyage, I'll always be on your side, as in the past, as much as I can. But since we're on the subject, I would like you to tell me clearly, in all honesty, if you still feel as sure as in the beginning that you will find land and people in this part of the world, or if, after so much time and experience to the contrary, you are beginning to have doubts.

COLUMBUS. Frankly and in confidence, as friend to friend, I confess that I'm beginning to feel a little unsure, especially because during this voyage, many of the signs which had given me great hope have proved empty – like the birds that flew overhead from the West, a few days after we left Gomera, and which I thought an indication of land nearby. Also, day after day, I have seen that the facts have not borne out the assumptions and predictions I had made before setting out to sea as to the various things that I believed would occur in the course of the voyage. So I'm beginning to think that, as these predictions have misled me – although they seemed almost infallible – it may also be that the main assumption, that we would find land on the other side of the ocean, will prove empty too. It is true that this assumption is so well founded that, if it is false, it would seem that we could not trust any human judgment except when it is based entirely on things we can actually see and touch. But, on the other hand, I realize that often, in fact most of the time, reality is at odds with theory. And I also ask myself, how can you know that each part of the world is so much like the others that, simply because the Eastern Hemisphere is occupied partly by land and partly by water, it must also follow that the Western Hemisphere is divided up between the two elements? How can you know that it is not totally occupied by one immense sea? Or that instead of land, or even land and water, it could not contain some other element? And if it is made of land and sea like the other, wouldn't it be possible that it is uninhabited? Or even uninhabitable? But suppose it is no less inhabited than ours; how can you be sure that there are rational creatures, as in ours? And even if there are, how can you be sure they are men and not some other kind of intelligent animals? And if they are men, that they are not quite different from those you know? Let's say, much bigger in body, much stronger, with much greater agility, naturally endowed with much greater intelligence and wit; also much better civilized and far more advanced in both art and science? This is what I keep asking myself. And after all, Nature is imbued with such power, and her effects are so varied and numerous that not only can we not judge with certainty what she has done and is doing in faraway places totally unknown to our world, but we may also wonder if it is not a grave mistake to argue the former on the basis of the latter. And it would not be against the probability of truth to imagine that the things of the unknown world – either all together or in part – are alien and wondrous to us. Here we see with our own eyes that in these waters the compass needle deflects from the North Star quite a bit toward the West – a novel phenomenon unheard of to seamen before now; and no matter how long I ponder, I cannot find a reason that satisfies me. For all this, however, I do not mean to imply that we should lend an ear to the fables of the ancients about the wonders of the unknown world and of this ocean, as, for instance, Hanno's fable about the countries filled with flames at night and about the rivers of fire flowing headlong into the sea. Indeed, we see how empty so far have been all the fears of dreadful prodigies and terrifying novelties felt by our men during this voyage – as when they saw that great mass of seaweed that seemed to turn the water into a meadow, somewhat obstructing our path, and they thought they had reached the ultimate limits of the navigable sea. But in answer to your question, I only mean to suggest that my assumption is based on the most probable arguments, not only in my judgment but in the judgment of many distinguished geographers, astronomers, and navigators, whom I have consulted, as you know, in Spain, Italy, and Portugal. Yet it might happen to be incorrect, for, as I repeat, many conclusions drawn from the best reasoning do not stand the test of experience, and this occurs more than ever when they concern things which are quite obscure to us.

GUTIERREZ. Then, in effect, you have staked your life, and the lives of your companions, on an issue that has no more basis than a purely speculative assumption.

COLUMBUS. That's true. I can't deny it. But leaving aside the fact that every day men risk their lives for much smaller causes and for matters of very little value – and even without giving it any thought – consider this: if you and I and our companions were not on these ships in the middle of this sea, in this unknown solitude, in as uncertain and dangerous a condition as we can imagine, what other kind of life would we be living? What would we be doing? How would we be spending these days? More happily, perhaps? Or, rather, wouldn't we be in some anxiety or hardship – or filled with boredom? What is a condition free from uncertainty and danger? If content and happy, it is to be preferred to any other; if tedious and miserable, I don't see what other kind of condition would be less desirable. I won't remind you of the glory and the benefits we will reap, should the outcome equal our hopes. Even if we don't gain any other advantage from this voyage, it still seems most profitable to me insofar as for some time it keeps us free from boredom, makes life dear to us, makes many things valuable to us which we might have otherwise held in low esteem. The ancients write – as you have probably read or heard – that unhappy lovers, hurling themselves into the sea from the Rock of Santa Maura (which was then called the Leucadian Rock) and surviving, were freed from the amorous passion by the grace of Apollo. I don't know whether we should believe that they were thus cured, but I know well that after escaping such a danger, they must have briefly held dear the very life they previously hated, even without Apollo's favor; or, in any case, they must have held it dearer and more valuable than before. In my judgment, every sea voyage is almost like a leap from the Leucadian Rock, and it produces effects which, although the same, are more lasting. In this sense, a sea voyage is far superior. It is commonly believed that being constantly in danger of death, seamen and soldiers value their own life much less than other people. But for the same reason I believe that very few people love and value their life as much as seamen and soldiers. How many blessings we ignore only because we have them! How many things that cannot even be called blessings seem very dear and very precious to seamen only because they are deprived of them! Who ever counted among human blessings having a little land to stand on? No one except seamen and, above all, ourselves, who, because of the great uncertainty about the outcome of this voyage, have no greater desire than the sight of a bit of land. This is the first thought that comes to us when we awaken, with this thought we fall asleep, and if from afar we happen to discover the tip of a mountain or a forest or a similar thing, we will not be able to contain our joy; and having set foot on land, only the thought of finding ourselves again on solid ground and of being able to go here and there walking as we please will make us feel full of bliss for several days.

GUTIERREZ. All this is quite correct, so much so that if your speculative assumption proves as true as your justification for having followed it, we shall no doubt enjoy this bliss – one day or another.

COLUMBUS. Personally, although I no longer dare promise it to myself with certainty, I hope, nevertheless, that we will soon enjoy it. For several days, as you know, the sounding line has been touching bottom; and the nature of what it brings to the surface seems a good sign to me. Toward evening, the clouds around the sun appear different in form and in color from those of the past days. The air, as you can feel, has become a little milder and warmer than in the past. The wind has no longer been blowing so full, and straight, and steady, but rather uncertain and variable as if it were interrupted by some obstacle. Add to this that reed floating in the sea which has apparently been recently cut and that little branch with its fresh red berries. And then the flocks of birds . . . they have misled me before, but there are so many of them now and so large and they grow so much in number from day to day that I feel we can somewhat rely on them, especially because there are among them some birds which do not seem to be shaped like marine birds. In short, as much as I try to restrain myself, all these signs together give me great and good expectations.

GUTIERREZ. This time God grant that it come true.

In Praise of Birds

One spring morning, Amelius, the solitary philosopher, was sitting with his books in the shade of his country house, reading. Struck by the singing of birds all around, he gradually began to listen and think, and he stopped reading. Finally, he took up his pen, and then and there he wrote what follows.

Birds are by nature the most joyous creatures in the world. I do not mean this in the sense that they always bring you joy whenever you see or hear them but that they themselves feel joy and gaiety more than any other animals. The other animals normally look serious and grave, and many of them even appear melancholy; they seldom give signs of joy, and when they do, these are slight and brief; during most of their enjoyment and pleasures they do not show exhilaration or any indication of gaiety. Even if they derive pleasure from the green fields, from the open and beautiful vistas, from the brilliant sunshine, from the crystalline and sweet air, they do not give any outward sign of it – except for the hares, about which it is said that at night when the moon shines, and especially when it is a full moon, they hop and play together, rejoicing in that brightness, as Xenophon writes. Mostly, birds show themselves extremely joyous in their movements and in their looks; and their virtue of bringing us gaiety by their presence comes only from the fact that their forms and their actions are always such that by nature they display a special ability and a special disposition for pleasure and joy – an appearance not to be deemed empty and deceptive. With every pleasure and satisfaction they experience, they sing; and the greater the pleasure or the satisfaction, the greater the vigor and the effort they put into their singing. And since they sing a great deal of the time, we must conclude that normally they are cheerful and enjoy life. And although it has been observed that when they are in love they sing better and more often and at greater lengths than at other times, it must not be believed that they are not moved to singing by other pleasures and other satisfactions than those of love. For we can clearly see that on a calm and serene day they sing more than on a dark and turbulent one; and during a storm they keep silent as they do any other time they are assailed by fear; and after a storm, they come out into the air singing and playing with one another. Similarly, we can see that they are used to singing in the morning when they wake, being moved partly by the gaiety they derive from the new day and partly by the pleasure, common to all animals, of feeling restored and refreshed by sleep. Likewise, they highly enjoy cheerful verdures, fertile vales, pure and transparent waters, beautiful landscapes. It is quite interesting that what appears agreeable and beautiful to us appears the same to them – as may be ascertained by the lures with which they are drawn into nets or birdlime in the hunting thickets and the like. It may also be ascertained from the nature of those places in the countryside that are most frequented by birds and where their singing is continuous and fervid. On the other hand, either none or very few of the other animals, except perhaps those that are domesticated and are used to living with men, share with us this notion of the amenity and the beauty of places. This should not be surprising, for they find pleasure only in what is natural. Now, in these things, a very large part of what we call natural is not so but is, in fact, rather artificial; thus cultivated fields, trees, and other plants trained and disposed in a certain order, rivers confined within precise boundaries and directed toward a definite course, and similar things have neither the condition nor the appearance they would have naturally. So that the aspect of every country inhabited by generations of civilized men – even if we do not consider the cities and other places where men congregate to live together – is something artificial and very different from what it would be in nature. Some people say, and it would bear on this subject, that the voice of birds is softer and sweeter and their singing more modulated in our areas than where men are wild and primitive; and they conclude that birds, even being free, pick up a little of the civilization of those men whose quarters they frequent.

Whether these people speak the truth or not, it certainly was a remarkable provision of nature to assign to the same species of animals both song and flight; so that those whose job it was to amuse the other living beings with their voices should normally be in high places, from which the sound could spread about through a greater space and reach a larger number of listeners, so that the air, which is the element destined for sound, should be peopled with vocal and musical creatures. We truly draw great consolation and pleasure – and we men no more, in my opinion, than the other animals – from listening to the singing of birds. And I think that this comes mainly not from the sweetness of the sounds, no matter how great they are, nor from their variety, nor from their mutual resonance, but from that gaiety which is naturally contained in song in general and in the song of birds in particular. Which is, so to speak, a sort of laughter, uttered by the birds when they feel well and comfortable.

Thus in some way it might be said that birds share with man the privilege of laughter – a privilege the other animals do not have. In fact, some people thought that since man is defined as an intellectual and reasoning animal, he could no less adequately be defined as a laughing animal, for they believed that laughter is no less characteristic of man than reason. And this is indeed something to marvel at: that man, who is the most afflicted and the most miserable of all creatures, should possess the faculty of laughter, which is alien to every other animal. And also something to marvel at is the use we make of this faculty, for we see many in extremely severe accidents, others in the depths of sadness, and still others who scarcely retain any love for life at all, totally convinced as they are of the vanity of every human good, almost incapable of any joy, and deprived of all hope – and yet we see them laugh. As a matter of fact, the more they know the vanity of those goods and the unhappiness of life, and the less they can hope and the less they are suited for the enjoyment of pleasure, the more men are inclined to laughter. Yet the nature of laughter in general and its inner principles and modes, as regards that

part of it which consists in the mind, can scarcely be
defined and explained – except by saying that laughter is
a form of temporary madness, raving, and delirium. For
men, never being satisfied and never finding real pleasure
in anything, cannot have a reasonable and just cause for
laughter. It would also be interesting to investigate how
and on what most probable occasion men first used and
recognized this power of theirs. For there is no doubt
that in a primitive condition, they generally appear serious, as do the other animals; and they even look melancholy. Thus, I am of the opinion that not only did laughter
appear in the world after tears – as to which there cannot
be any controversy – but that it took a good space of time
before it was first experimented with and seen. And during that time neither did the mother smile at her child,
nor did the child recognize her with a smile – as Virgil
says. For if nowadays, and at least where people have
become civilized, men begin to laugh shortly after they
are born, they do so mainly as a result of example because
they see others laugh. I would think that the first occasion
and the first cause for men to laugh was drunkenness –
which is also inherently characteristic of the human race.
This originated long before men attained any kind of
civilization; in fact, we know that there can scarcely be
found any people so primitive who have not provided
themselves with some beverage or some other means to
inebriate themselves and who are not in the habit of
doing so immoderately. This should not be surprising,
for as men are unhappy beyond all other animals, so more
than all others do they find pleasure in every painless alien-
ation of the mind, in forgetting about themselves, in an

interruption, so to speak, of life. And so, by suspending, or in some way decreasing, the sense and knowledge of their own ills, they receive no small benefit. And as to laughter, we can observe that, although they are of serious and sad appearance at other times, primitive people laugh profusely when drunk – talking abundantly and singing, contrary to their habits. But I will discuss these matters more extensively in a history of laughter, which I have in mind to write. After investigating its birth, I will proceed by narrating its exploits, its vicissitudes, and its fortunes, up to the present time – when it is given more dignity and power than ever before by holding a place in civilized nations, by performing a function through which in some way it assumes the roles previously played by virtue, justice, honor, and the like, and in many ways by restraining and frightening men from evil actions. Now, to conclude on the singing of birds, I will say that since we generally draw consolation and gaiety from the joy we see or know in others – if we do not envy them – Nature very laudably decided that the singing of birds, which is an expression of gaiety and a kind of laughter, should be public whereas the singing and the laughter of man, with respect to the rest of the world, are private; and she wisely saw to it that the earth and air should swarm with animals that continuously give out resonant and solemn sounds, as though to applaud universal life and incite other living creatures to gaiety, thereby bearing uninterrupted, though false, witness to the happiness of all things.

And that birds are and show themselves to be more joyous than the other animals is not without a profound reason. For as I implied at the beginning, Nature really made them better suited for pleasure and happiness. First of all, they do not seem to be subject to boredom. They change place every moment; they pass from one region to another, however remote, and from the lowest to the highest realms of the air, in a brief space of time and with prodigious ease; in the course of their lives they see and experience things that are infinite in number and most diverse in form; they continuously exercise their bodies; they greatly abound in open-air activities. All the other animals, when they have provided for their needs, like to sit quietly and leisurely; not one of them, with the possible exception of fish and also some flying insects, goes running about for sheer amusement. Similarly, primitive man – who hardly takes a step except to keep providing for his daily needs which demand but little and short work, or except when a storm, or some wild beast or another similar event drives him – likes mainly leisure and apathy; he consumes almost his entire day sitting indolently and silently inside his little shapeless hut, in the open air, or in the clefts and caverns of cliffs and rocks. Birds, on the contrary, remain in the same place for a very short while; they continuously come and go without any need whatsoever; they fly around for pleasure; and sometimes they enjoy flying hundreds of miles from the area where they usually stay, and then they return there the evening of the same day. Even during the short time they stay in one place, you will never see them sit still; they keep turning here and there, strolling about, bending, stretching their necks, shaking, fluttering with liveliness, agility, and an indescribable swiftness of movement. In short, from when a bird is unlocked from the egg until it dies, save for the intervals of sleep, it is never at rest for a moment. As a result of these observations, it seems apparent that by nature the normal state of the other animals, including men, is rest; of birds, movement.

To these qualities and external conditions correspond the internal ones, that is to say, those of the mind – which make them better suited for happiness than other animals. Their sense of hearing is extremely sharp, and their eyesight is so efficient and perfect that our minds can hardly imagine it; because of these powers they enjoy all day long immense and most diversified spectacles, and from high up they discover at once so great an expanse of land and distinctly perceive so many regions with their eyes as man can hardly comprehend at the same time; from which we must infer that they must possess very great strength and vivacity and very great power of imagination. Not of that kind of profound, fervid, and tempestuous imagination as Dante and Tasso possessed – which is a most fatal gift and the origin of most grievous and perpetual anxiety and anguish – but of the kind that is rich, varied, light, unstable, and childlike, which is the most abundant source of pleasant and joyful thoughts, sweet illusions, manifold pleasures and consolations; it is also the greatest and the most fruitful gift Nature can generously bestow on living souls. Thus, birds possess in great abundance what in this faculty is good and conducive to mental happiness without what is noxious and painful. And since they abound in external life, they are equally rich in the internal but in such a way that this abundance brings them advantages and pleasures, as with children – not disadvantages and misery, as generally with men. For as in their liveliness and outward mobility birds manifestly resemble children, so we may reasonably assume that they resemble them in their inner qualities as well. And were the blessings of childhood common to the other ages and the ills of these no greater than those of childhood itself, perhaps man would have cause to bear life patiently.

In my opinion, if considered in certain ways, the nature of birds surpasses in perfection the nature of the other animals. For example, if we consider that birds by far excel all the others in eyesight and in the faculty of hearing, which, according to the natural order concerning living creatures, are the principal senses, it then follows that the nature of birds is more perfect than the other natures of living creatures. Additionally, if, as we have seen, other animals are naturally inclined to rest and birds to movement – and movement is more alive than rest, life consisting actually in movement, while birds abound in external movement more than any other animal – and moreover, if eyesight and hearing, in which they excel all the others and which predominate among their powers, are the two senses most characteristic of the living, for they also are more vivid and mobile both in themselves as in the habits and other effects that they produce inwardly and outwardly in the animal; and, finally, if we consider the other things already mentioned, the conclusion follows that birds have more external and internal life than the other animals. Now, if life is more perfect than its opposite, at least in living creatures, and if, therefore, a greater abundance of life is greater perfection, also here it follows that the nature of birds is more perfect. At this point we cannot forget that birds are equally suited to withstand the extremes of cold and heat, even without any interval of time between one and the other. In fact, we often see that in little more than an instant, from the ground they soar through the air to very great altitudes, which is like saying to extremely cold areas, and in a short time many of them fly across a variety of climates.

Finally, as Anacreon wished he could be changed into a mirror to be continuously looked at by his beloved, or into a skirt to cover her, or into an ointment to anoint her, or into water to wash her, or into a breast band so that she would press him to her bosom, or into a pearl which she would wear around her neck, or into a shoe that at least she might press him with her foot – similarly, I would like to be changed for a while into a bird so that I could experience the contentment and the joy of their life.

Song of
the Great Wild Rooster

Some Hebrew scholars and writers assert that between
the sky and the earth, or rather half in one and half in the
other, there lives a certain wild rooster, whose feet rest
on the earth and whose crest and beak touch the sky. In
addition to such peculiarities of his as can be read in those
authors, this giant rooster has the use of reason; or,
indeed, like a parrot, it has been taught by I know not
whom to utter words in the manner of men. In fact, a
song entitled *Scir detarnegòl bara letzafra*, that is to say,
Morning Song of the Great Wild Rooster, written in Hebrew
script and in a language mixed with Chaldean, Targumic,
Rabbinic, Cabalistic, and Talmudic, was found in an
ancient parchment. I have managed to understand it and to
translate it into our vernacular as follows, not without
great labor or without consulting various rabbis, cabalists,
theologians, jurists, and Jewish philosophers. I have not
been able to ascertain as yet whether this song is repeated
by the rooster from time to time or every morning;
whether it was sung only once; who hears it or who has
heard it; whether its language is actually the language of
the rooster or whether the song itself was translated
from another tongue. As to the present rendering, I have
sought in every way I could to make it as faithful as possible, and I have thought it best to use prose rather than
verse, notwithstanding the fact that it was poetry. Its

somewhat disconnected and perhaps occasionally turgid style should not be held against me, for it conforms to that of the original text, which in this respect corresponds to the norms of Oriental languages and especially of their poets.

Up, mortals, awake! The day is born again; truth returns to earth, and empty images depart. Arise; take up again the burden of life; return from the false to the real world!

This is the time when everyone collects and reviews in his mind all the thoughts of his present life, recalls to memory his plans, efforts, and affairs, represents to himself the pleasures and the afflictions that might come to him during the new day. And each one during this time wishes more than ever to find in his mind joyous expectations and pleasant thoughts. But very few are granted this wish. For to awake is unfortunate for everyone. No sooner are the wretched awakened than they fall back into the hands of their unhappiness. Sweetest of all things is that sleep which was brought about by a combination of joy and hope – which are both preserved whole and safe until the coming of day, but then they both fail or dwindle.

If the sleep of mortals were perpetual and one and the same with life; if under the day star all living creatures languished in the most profound quiet all over the earth and there appeared no activity whatever: no lowing of oxen in the meadows, no roar of wild beasts in the forests, no singing of birds in the air, no murmur of butterflies nor buzzing of bees throughout the countryside, no voice, no movement arose in any place but that of waters, winds, and storms; then the universe would indeed be useless; but would there perhaps be in it a lesser quantity of happiness or a larger amount of misery than there is now? I ask you, O Sun, author of the day and guardian of our waking hours, in the course of the centuries that you have so far measured and consumed rising and setting, did you once see a single one of the living beings happy? Of the innumerable works of the mortals which you have seen until now, do you think that even one achieved its aim: the satisfaction, continuous or temporary, of the creature that had produced it? Rather, do you see now, or did you ever see, happiness within the confines of the world? In what field does it dwell, in what forest, on what mountain, in what valley, in what region inhabited or deserted, in what planet of the many your flames light up and warm? Maybe it hides from your sight or resides in the depths of the caverns or in the bosom of the earth or at the bottom of the sea? What living thing, what plant or anything else you give life to, what creature endowed with, or deprived of, vegetative or animal life partakes of it? And you yourself, who, like an indefatigable giant, night and day, without either sleep or respite, swiftly run the immeasurable path that is prescribed to you, are you happy or unhappy?

Mortals awake! You are not yet free from life. The time will come when no external force, no internal movement, will shake you from the quiet of sleep, in which you will then forever insatiably rest. Death is not granted to you as yet; only occasionally are you allowed a semblance of it for a short space of time. For life could not be sustained if it were not frequently interrupted. Too long a want of this brief and ephemeral sleep is in itself deadly and a cause of eternal sleep. Such a thing is life that in order to bear it, we must lay it down, now and again, to catch our breath and to refresh ourselves with a taste and almost a particle of death.

The very essence of things seems to have death as its real and only purpose. All that exists springs from nothingness, because what does not exist cannot die. It is certain that the ultimate purpose of existence is not happiness, for nothing is happy. It is true that living creatures aim at this end with every one of their works; but they do not attain it through any one of them; and during their entire lives they keep striving, straining themselves, and suffering without agonizing and without toiling toward anything but the achievement of this sole purpose of nature, which is death.

The first hours of the day are normally the most endurable for the living. Few people find their minds occupied by pleasant and joyous thoughts when they awake; but almost everyone produces and forms some rather quickly; for at that hour the human mind, although without any specific and particular reason, is above all inclined to cheerfulness and more disposed than at any other time to tolerate the ills of life. Therefore, if someone was filled with despair when caught by sleep, he again finds hope in his mind when he awakens, even if there is no reason for it. Many misfortunes and personal troubles, many causes for fear and for distress appear at that time much smaller than the night before. Also, often the anguish of the past day is scorned and almost laughed at as the result of illusions and of empty imagining. The evening is comparable to old age, while the beginning of the morning is like youth, which is generally at ease and confident; and the evening is sad, discouraged, and inclined to ominous expectations. But just as actual youth in life, so the one mortals experience every day is extremely brief and ephemeral; and very soon the day too grows older.

Although it is the best part of life, the flower of our years is yet a rather miserable thing. In fact, even this paltry blessing fails in such a short time that when man notices by many signs that it is declining, he has scarcely experienced the perfection of his being, or has hardly been able to feel and know his own powers when they already begin to diminish. Mortal creatures of all kinds spend the greatest part of life withering away. So much is nature intent upon pointing to death in all her works: for no other reason does old age prevail so manifestly and for so long a time in life and in the world. Every part of the universe hastens indefatigably toward death with marvellous determination and swiftness. Only the universe itself appears immune to decaying and to languishing; for if in the fall and in the winter it shows itself almost infirm and old, nevertheless, it always grows young again in the new season. But just as mortals in the first part of the day reacquire some portion of their youth and yet grow older every day and finally expire, so the universe may appear to grow young again at the beginning of every year, although it nevertheless continuously grows older. The time will come when this universe and nature herself will be no more. And just as of very great human kingdoms and empires and of their marvelous exploits, which were so very famous in other ages, there remains no sign of fame whatsoever; so too of the entire world, and of the infinite vicissitudes and calamities of all created things, no single trace will remain; but a naked silence and a most profound quiet will fill the immensity of space. Thus, this stupendous and frightening mystery of universal existence, before it can be declared or understood, will vanish and be lost.

The Copernicus

Scene One
THE FIRST HOUR AND THE SUN

FIRST HOUR. Good morning, Your Excellency.

SUN. Yes, rather, good night.

FIRST HOUR. The horses are ready.

SUN. Good.

FIRST HOUR. The morning star has been out for some time.

SUN. Let her come and go as she likes.

FIRST HOUR. What do you mean by that, Your Excellency?

SUN. I mean that I want you to leave me alone.

FIRST HOUR. But, Your Excellency, the night has already lasted so long that it can't last any longer. If we wait any more, Your Excellency, something really strange might happen.

SUN. Whatever happens, I'm not going to move.

FIRST HOUR. Oh, Your Excellency, what's that? Don't you feel well?

SUN. No, no, I'm not feeling anything. I just don't want to move. And you, you mind your own business.

FIRST HOUR. How can I, if you don't come? I'm the first hour of the day; and how can the day be, if Your Excellency isn't kind enough to come out as usual?

73

SUN. If not to the day, you'll belong to the night – or the Hours of the night will work a double shift, and you and your day companions will do nothing. Because, do you know what? I'm tired of this continuous going around to give light to a few little animals that live on a handful of mud – so small that I, who have quite good eyesight, can't even see it. Tonight I have decided that I don't want to take any more trouble for this; and if men want to see some light, they should keep their fires burning or find some other way.

FIRST HOUR. But, Your Excellency, what way do you want them to find, those poor little creatures? And to have to keep their lamps burning or to keep so many candles lit the whole space of the day will be excessively costly. If they had already found that kind of air to be used for burning, for lighting streets, rooms, shops, cellars, and everything else, at a very low cost, then I would say that it wouldn't be so bad. But the fact is that three hundred years, more or less, still have to pass before men find this kind of remedy. Meanwhile, they'll run out of oil, and of wax, and of pitch, and of tallow; and they'll have nothing more to burn.

SUN. They can go and catch fireflies and glowworms.

FIRST HOUR. And what will they do against the cold? For without Your Excellency's assistance, the firewood of all the forests won't be enough to keep them warm. They'll also starve to death, for the earth will no longer bear fruit. And so in the course of a few years, even the breed of those poor animals will be lost. And when they'll have gone groping here and there about the earth for a while, looking for something to eat and to keep warm, finally, after there is nothing left to swallow and when the last spark of fire is no more, they'll all die in the dark, frozen like pieces of rock crystal.

SUN. Why should I care? Am I, by any chance, the wet nurse of the human race, or the chef who must prepare and cook their food? And why should I care if a few invisible little creatures, millions of miles away, can't see and can't stand the cold without my light? And then, if I must also serve, so to speak, as a heater or a fireplace for this human family, it's only reasonable that if the family wants to warm themselves, they should come to the fireplace, and not that the fireplace should go running around the house. So, if the earth needs my presence, let her go moving around herself and do everything possible to get it; for, personally, I don't need anything from the earth that I should go and look out for her.

FIRST HOUR. Your Excellency means to say, if I understand well, that now the earth should do what you have been doing in the past.

SUN. Yes, now, and forever from now on.

FIRST HOUR. Your Excellency is certainly right there, in addition to the fact that you can do whatever you like. Nevertheless, please consider how many beautiful things will necessarily go to rack and ruin if you establish this new order of things. The day will no longer have its beautiful gilded chariot, with its beautiful horses, that used to bathe in the sea; and without dwelling on other details, we poor Hours will no longer have a place in the sky, and from celestial maidens we'll become terrestrial, unless, as I expect, we dissolve into smoke. But be this as it may, the problem will be to convince the earth to go around, which must be quite difficult, for she is not used to it; and it must also seem strange to her to have to run forever and exert herself so much, after never having moved an inch from that place of hers. And if Your Excellency is seemingly beginning to lend an ear to laziness, I've heard that the earth is in no way more inclined to physical exertion now than she was in the past.

SUN. In this case, need will goad her and make her jump and run as much as necessary. But here the fastest and surest way is to find a poet or a natural philosopher who would convince the earth to move or, in case he couldn't convince her, who would force her to. For in the long run, most of this business is in the hands of poets and of natural philosophers; as a matter of fact, they can do nearly anything. The poets are those who in the past (when I was younger and listened to them), with those beautiful songs of theirs, led me – big and fat as I am – to do of my own free will, as a sport or an honorable exercise, that extremely stupid job of running desperately around a small grain of sand. But now that I'm older and have turned to philosophy, in everything I look for what's useful and not for what's beautiful; and the sentiments of poets, when they don't make me sick, make me laugh. Before doing something, I want to have good and substantial reasons; and since I find no reason whatsoever for considering an active life preferable to a leisurely and pleasant one – for an active life could not give you any fruit worth the trouble or even the thought (in the world there is no fruit worth a penny) – I've resolved to leave the exertions and the discomforts to others and, as far as I'm concerned, live at home in peace and without doing anything. Besides being partly the effect of age, this change, as I told you, was caused by philosophers – people who these days have begun to gain power, and keep gaining it more and more. Therefore, if I want the earth to move and to run around in my place, in one respect a poet would be more suitable than a natural philosopher or a scientist, for poets, with one story or another, make people believe that the things of the world are really valuable and important and that they are very pleasant and beautiful, and they create a thousand cheerful hopes, and thus they persuade people to exert themselves and work hard, whereas philosophers dissuade them. However, since philosophers have begun to get the upper hand, I'm afraid that nowadays a poet would not be listened to by the earth any more than by me; or if he were listened to, he wouldn't have any effect. Therefore, I think it's better if we enlist the services of a natural philosopher or a scientist, for although philosophers are normally little suited, and still less inclined, to persuade others to work, it might nevertheless happen that in this extreme case they would manage to do something totally unusual – unless the earth decides that it is more advantageous to go to perdition rather than to trouble herself so much – in which case I wouldn't say that she is wrong. Enough, we'll see what happens. Now, do this: go down to the earth, or send one of your sisters, anyone you want; and if she finds one of those natural philosophers outside his house in the fresh air, studying the sky and the stars – for it is reasonable to expect that she will find some because of the extraordinary length of this night – without more ado, she should lift him up, throw him on her back, and bring him all the way up here to me; and I'll persuade him to do what's necessary. Do you understand?

FIRST HOUR. Yes, Your Excellency. I'll do just that.

Scene Two
(Standing on his terrace, watching the eastern sky through a small paper tube – because the telescope had not been invented yet)

COPERNICUS. Incredible. Either the clocks are all wrong, or the sun should have already risen more than an hour ago; and yet here we can't even see the faintest glimmer in the east, although the sky is as clear and limpid as a mirror. All the stars are shining as if it were midnight. Now go and check Almagest and Sacrobosco, and ask them to explain the reason for this. I have often heard about the night Jupiter spent with Amphitryon's wife; I also remember having recently read in a modern book by a Spaniard that the Peruvians say that once in ancient times there was in their country an extremely long night, as a matter of fact an interminable one, and that finally the sun came out of a lake they call Titicaca. But until now I thought that this was sheer nonsense; and just like all reasonable men I was sure that it was so. Now that I realize that reason and science aren't worth an iota, I have decided to believe that those, and similar things, may be perfectly true. In fact, I'm about to go to all the lakes and all the swamps I can find, to see if I can, by any chance, fish out the sun. But what's this roar that I hear – like the sound of the wings of a great bird?

Scene Three
THE LAST HOUR AND COPERNICUS

LAST HOUR. Copernicus, I'm the Last Hour.

COPERNICUS. The last hour? Well, I can't do anything about it. Only, if possible, give me enough time to write my last will and put my affairs in order – before I die.

LAST HOUR. What do you mean, 'die'? I'm not the last hour of life.

COPERNICUS. Who are you then? The last canonical hour of the breviary?

LAST HOUR. I certainly believe that you like that one better than the others – when you are in the choir.

COPERNICUS. But how do you know that I'm a canon priest? And how do you know me? You just called me by my name.

LAST HOUR. I got information about you from some people down below in the street. In short, I'm the last hour of the day.

COPERNICUS. Ah, I understand. The First Hour is ill; that's why we don't see the day yet.

LAST HOUR. Allow me to go on. The day won't come any more – not today, not tomorrow, not ever, if you don't do something about it.

COPERNICUS. That's a good one! As if it were my job to make the day!

LAST HOUR. I'll tell you how. But first you must come with me immediately to the house of the Sun, my master. You'll learn more along the way, and His Excellency will tell you part of it himself when we get there.

COPERNICUS. All right. But if I'm not mistaken, the trip must be a rather long one. And how can I carry enough supplies so that I won't starve to death some years before I get there? Besides, I don't think His Excellency's lands produce enough for a single lunch.

LAST HOUR. Forget about these fears. You won't have to stay in the house of the Sun for long; and the trip will take but a moment – for in case you don't know, I'm a spirit.

COPERNICUS. But I'm a body.

LAST HOUR. Well, there's no need for you to worry about these things; you're not a metaphysical philosopher. Come here, get on my shoulders, and leave the rest to me.

COPERNICUS. Well, here we go . . . Let's see how this thing is going to end.

Scene Four

COPERNICUS AND THE SUN

COPERNICUS. Most illustrious sir.

SUN. Forgive me, Copernicus, if I don't ask you to sit down; but we don't use chairs. We'll be done in a moment. You've already heard from my servant what this problem is all about. Personally – and from what the girl tells me about your ability – I think you are perfectly suited for the job we have in mind.

COPERNICUS. Sir, I see many difficulties in this job.

SUN. Difficulties should not frighten a man of your kind. As a matter of fact, people say that they increase the courage of the courageous. But then, what are these difficulties?

COPERNICUS. First of all, no matter how great is the power of natural philosophy or science, I'm not sure it's so great as to convince the earth to begin to run rather than sit comfortably, and to work and exert her-self rather than remain idle, especially in our times, which are not heroic at all.

SUN. So, if you can't convince her, force her.

COPERNICUS. Gladly, my illustrious sir, if I were a Hercules or even a Roland, and not a canon priest from Worms.

SUN. What has that got to do with it? Aren't we told that one of your ancient mathematicians used to say that if he could stand somewhere outside the world, no doubt he could move heaven and earth? Now, you don't have to move heaven; and here you are in a place outside the earth. Therefore, if you're no less clever than that ancient one, you should be able to move her – whether she likes it or not.

COPERNICUS. My dear sir, I could do that, but I would need a lever, which should be so long that not only I, but you yourself, illustrious sir, however rich you may be, wouldn't have enough to cover the cost of the neces-sary materials and of the labor. Another, and graver, difficulty is the following: as a matter of fact, it's like a knot of difficulties. Up to now the earth has held first place in the universe, that is to say, the center; and, as you know, she has been sitting motionless without anything else to do but look around at all the other globes of the universe, the largest as well as the smallest, the shiny as well as the dark, which have kept rolling above and below and by her sides with such a hurry, such a concern, such a vehemence that we are stunned if we just think about it. And, thus, everything proved to be at her services, and the universe looked like a court where the earth sat as if on a throne, and the other globes all around her, like courtiers, guards, and lackeys, tending to one job or another. As a result, the earth has always believed herself to be the empress of the universe; and, actually, while conditions remained as they were in the past, we can't say that hers was an unreasonable idea; as a matter of fact, I wouldn't deny that such an idea of hers rested on good foundations. And then what shall I tell you about men? We consider, and shall always consider, ourselves the first and the supremely important among all earthly creatures. Each one of us, even if dressed in rags and with no more than a piece of hard bread to gnaw on, thinks of himself as an emperor; and not just of Constantinople or of Germany or of half the earth – as the Roman emperors were – but as an emperor of the universe, an emperor of the sun, of the planets, of all the stars, visible and invisible, and the ultimate cause of the stars, of the planets, of your illustrious Excellency, and of all things. But now if we want the earth to abandon that central place, if we make her run, revolve, bustle about continuously, do exactly the same job as has so far been done by the other globes, and, finally, become one of the planets – this will mean that her earthly majesty, and their human majesties, will have to clear the throne and abandon the empire – being left with their rags and their miseries, which aren't few.

SUN. What are you driving at with this talk, my dear Father Nicholas? Are you perhaps afraid that such an action would be high treason?

COPERNICUS. No, most illustrious sir; for neither the codes, nor the Digest, nor the books of public law, nor those of imperial law, nor of civil law, nor of natural law, mention this kind of treason, as far as I can remember. But I mean to say that this business of ours is not going to be simply material, as it appears at first sight, and that its effects are not going to be restricted to physics, for it will upset all the steps on the ladder of the dignity of things and the order of beings; it will switch the purposes of creatures; and therefore it will cause an extremely great revolution in metaphysics as well as in fact, in everything that touches the speculative side of knowledge. And as a result, if men can or want to reason well, they'll discover that they are something completely different from what they have been until now or from what they have imagined themselves to be.

SUN. Son, those things don't frighten me at all; for I respect metaphysics as much as physics, and as much as chemistry – or necromancy, if you like. And men will have to be satisfied with being what they are, and if they don't like that, let them go on with their upside-down reasoning and with their arguing against the evidence of facts, as they will be able to do very easily. Thus, they'll continue to believe they are whatever they think – either barons, or dukes, or emperors, or anything else they like. This will comfort them, and those judgments of theirs won't annoy me in the slightest.

COPERNICUS. All right, let's forget about men and about earth. But consider, my most illustrious sir, what we may expect to happen with the other planets. When they see that the earth has become one of them and does everything they do, they will no longer want to be so naked and unadorned, so deserted and sad as they have always been – with the earth alone having so many ornaments. They too will want their rivers, their seas, their mountains, their plants, and, among other things, their animals and their inhabitants; for they won't see any reason for being inferior to the earth in anything. And there will be another immense revolution in the universe: an endless number of new families will in a moment be seen springing up everywhere like mushrooms.

SUN. And you can let them spring up. And let them be as many as they can; for my light and my heat will be enough for all of them – and at no extra cost; and the universe will have enough to feed, clothe, lodge, and treat them generously without getting into debt.

COPERNICUS. But most illustrious sir, consider a little further, and you'll see yet another messy situation. The stars, too, when they see that you have sat down, not on a stool but on a throne, and that you are surrounded by such a beautiful court and such a population of planets – they, too, will want not only to sit down themselves and take a rest, but they'll want to reign as well; and in order to reign, one must have subjects; therefore, they'll want their own planets just as you have – each one his own. And these new planets will also have to be adorned and inhabited, like the earth. And at this point I won't tell you any more about the poor human race – which has already become almost nothing in relation to this present world. What will it become when so many thousands of other worlds burst forth so that the minutest star in the Milky Way won't be without one of her own? But even if we consider only your own interest, let me say that until now you have been, if not first, certainly second in the universe – let's say, next to the earth – and have had no equal, for the stars haven't had the audacity to compare themselves with you. But in this new state of the universe you'll have as many equals as there are stars with their worlds. So be careful that this change you want to make doesn't prejudice your own dignity.

SUN. Don't you remember what your Caesar said when, crossing the Alps, he happened to pass near the hamlet of some poor barbarians? – that he would rather be first in that little hamlet than second in Rome. Similarly, I should prefer to be first in this world of ours rather than second in the universe. But it isn't ambition that moves me to change the present state of things; it's only the love of peace or, to be more exact, laziness. And so, I don't much care about having or not having equals or about being in first or in last place; for unlike Cicero I'm more interested in leisure than in dignity.

COPERNICUS. Most illustrious sir, as far as I'm concerned, I'll do everything possible to get this leisure for you. But I'm afraid that even if I manage to succeed in my intent, it won't last very long. First, I'm almost sure that before many years have passed, you'll be forced to go whirling around like the pulley of a well or like a millstone – though without changing places. Then I suspect that finally, sooner or later, you'll find it necessary to begin to run again; I don't say around the earth; but what do you care about this? And perhaps that same revolving of yours will serve as a reason for your running. Enough, be it as it may; in spite of all difficulties and other considerations, if you insist in your resolution, I'll see if I can help you, so that if this doesn't work out, you'll believe that I could not – and not say that I'm a man without much courage.

SUN. All right, my Copernicus, try.

COPERNICUS. There is only one more difficulty.

SUN. Tell me, what's that?

COPERNICUS. I wouldn't like to be burned alive like the phoenix because of this. For if this happens, I'm sure that I wouldn't rise again from my ashes like that bird; and so, from then on I wouldn't see Your Excellency's face any more.

SUN. Listen, Copernicus, you know that at the time when you philosophers and scientists had scarcely been born – I mean to say, when poetry held the field – I was a prophet. Now I want you to let me predict the future for the last time, and in memory of my ancient power I want you to believe me. So then, I tell you that perhaps after you, those who approve what you have done may get somewhat charred or something like that; but you yourself, as far as I can see, won't suffer at all because of this. And if you want to be even safer, follow this advice: dedicate the book you write on the subject to the pope. This way, I promise you that you won't even lose your canonry.

Dialogue Between
an Almanac Peddler
and a Passer-by

PEDDLER. Almanacs, new almanacs; new calendars. Do you need any almanacs, Sir?

PASSER-BY. Almanacs for the new year?

PEDDLER. Yes, Sir.

PASSER-BY. Do you think the new year is going to be a happy one?

PEDDLER. Yes, Sir, absolutely.

PASSER-BY. Like last year?

PEDDLER. More, much more.

PASSER-BY. Like the year before?

PEDDLER. More, Sir, more.

PASSER-BY. But like what other? Wouldn't you want the new year to be like one of these past years?

PEDDLER. No, Sir, I wouldn't.

PASSER-BY. How many new years ago did you start selling almanacs?

PEDDLER. Sir, it must be twenty years.

PASSER-BY. Which one of those twenty years would you want the next one to be like?

PEDDLER. Me? I wouldn't know.

PASSER-BY. Don't you remember any year in particular that you thought was happy?

PEDDLER. Actually, I don't, Sir.

PASSER-BY. But life is beautiful, isn't it?

PEDDLER. Everybody knows that.

PASSER-BY. Wouldn't you like to live those twenty years over again, and all your past years, beginning with the day you were born?

PEDDLER. Eh, my dear Sir, I wish to God I could.

PASSER-BY. But if you had to live exactly the same life all over again – with all its pleasures and all its pains?

PEDDLER. I wouldn't like that.

PASSER-BY. But what kind of life would you like to live over again? The life I've had, or a prince's, or who else's? Don't you think that I, the prince, or anyone else, would answer just like you, that having to live the same life over again, no one would want to go back to it?

PEDDLER. I think so.

PASSER-BY. You wouldn't go back either, unless you could in some other way?

PEDDLER. No. Sir; I really wouldn't.

PASSER-BY. But what kind of life would you like then?

PEDDLER. Any kind, just as God would send it to me, with no other conditions.

PASSER-BY. Any life at random, without knowing anything about it in advance, just as we don't know anything about the new year?

PEDDLER. Precisely.

PASSER-BY. That's what I would like too if I were to live all over again; and that's what everyone would like. But this means that, up until the end of this year, Fortune has treated everyone badly. And it's clear that everyone thinks that he was allotted more, and greater, evil than good – if to live the same life all over again, with all its good and all its evil, no one would want to be born anew. The life that's beautiful is not the life we know, but the life we don't know; not the past life, but the future. With the new year, Fortune will start treating you and me and all the others well, and the happy life will begin. Isn't it true?

PEDDLER. Let's hope so.

PASSER-BY. Then show me your most beautiful almanac.

PEDDLER. Here it is, Sir. This one is thirty cents.

PASSER-BY. Here's thirty cents.

PEDDLER. Thank you, Sir. Goodbye. Almanacs, new almanacs; new calendars.

THE STORY OF PENGUIN CLASSICS

Before 1946 ... 'Classics' are mainly the domain of academics and students; readable editions for everyone else are almost unheard of. This all changes when a little-known classicist, E. V. Rieu, presents Penguin founder Allen Lane with the translation of Homer's *Odyssey* that he has been working on in his spare time.

1946 Penguin Classics debuts with *The Odyssey*, which promptly sells three million copies. Suddenly, classics are no longer for the privileged few.

1950s Rieu, now series editor, turns to professional writers for the best modern, readable translations, including Dorothy L. Sayers's *Inferno* and Robert Graves's unexpurgated *Twelve Caesars*.

1960s The Classics are given the distinctive black covers that have remained a constant throughout the life of the series. Rieu retires in 1964, hailing the Penguin Classics list as 'the greatest educative force of the twentieth century.'

1970s A new generation of translators swells the Penguin Classics ranks, introducing readers of English to classics of world literature from more than twenty languages. The list grows to encompass more history, philosophy, science, religion and politics.

1980s The Penguin American Library launches with titles such as *Uncle Tom's Cabin*, and joins forces with Penguin Classics to provide the most comprehensive library of world literature available from any paperback publisher.

1990s The launch of Penguin Audiobooks brings the classics to a listening audience for the first time, and in 1999 the worldwide launch of the Penguin Classics website extends their reach to the global online community.

The 21st Century Penguin Classics are completely redesigned for the first time in nearly twenty years. This world-famous series now consists of more than 1300 titles, making the widest range of the best books ever written available to millions – and constantly redefining what makes a 'classic'.

The Odyssey continues ...

The best books ever written

PENGUIN CLASSICS

SINCE 1946

PENGUIN BOOKS   *GREAT IDEAS*

Throughout history, some books have changed the world. They have transformed the way we see ourselves – and each other. They have inspired debate, dissent, war and revolution. They have enlightened, outraged, provoked and comforted. They have enriched lives – and destroyed them. Now PENGUIN brings you the works of the great thinkers, pioneers, radicals and visionaries whose ideas shook civilization and helped make us who we are.

Leopardi, poet and philosopher, explores in humorous but savage dialogue the power of fashion and its strange irrationality. He also imagines conversations between Hercules and Atlas, Nature and an Icelander, and the Earth and the Moon, as well as producing a simple essay praising the humble bird.

read more Ⓟ

ISBN 978-0-141-19255-0

9 780141 192550

penguinclassics.com

UK £4.99
CAN $9.99

Cover artwork:
Phil Baines